DISCARD

E=

Exploring the sky and sea
AUGUSTE AND JACQUES PICCARD

Britannica Bookshelf—Great Lives for Young Americans

Exploring the sky and sea

AUGUSTE AND JACQUES

PICCARD

by Alida Malkus

Illustrated by Robert Boehmer

Published by
BRITANNICA BOOKS
a division of
ENCYCLOPAEDIA BRITANNICA, INC., *Chicago*

TABLE OF CONTENTS

Exploring the sky and sea
AUGUSTE AND JACQUES PICCARD

Chapter 1

Up Into the Stratosphere

The great balloon swayed back and forth, tugging on the mooring ropes as though it were alive. It loomed against the sky, a vast, tapering, pear-shaped thing. A brisk ground wind was blowing, knocking the aluminum cabin about, tangling the ropes.

Auguste Piccard and his companion Paul Kipfer climbed into the spherical cabin and closed the hatch. The balloon strained at the ropes as if it could not wait to get off into the sky.

The flight handlers had fastened a restraining rope to the ground-maneuvering belt which was wrapped around the upper half of the balloon. The ground crew suddenly cast off the balloon without signaling the aeronauts inside the cabin. It was 3:45 in the morning.

The cables slipped through the mooring rings, the balloon was released, and it shot upward. Shouts of the spectators rose after the airship as it climbed higher and higher. The watchers had waited hours for this sensational first flight. The people of Augsburg, Germany, on this 27th day of May, 1931, were watching the result of years of planning and painstaking preparation being put to the test.

This huge balloon was like no other. It was specially designed to ascend into the stratosphere by the Swiss scientist and inventor, Piccard himself. It would withstand tremendous pressure, yet it was light enough to rise into the highly rarified air of the upper regions. Extremely light material weighing only 2 3/5 ounces per square yard was used in the upper three quarters of the sphere; an even lighter material weighing only 1 3/5 ounces per square yard was used for the lower quarter of the balloon. The entire surface of the balloon was covered with rubber that weighed only 2 4/5 ounces a square yard.

Until this time a net that completely covered the sphere of a balloon was considered indispensable, but Professor Piccard discarded the net covering because of its extra weight. And too, a net would interfere with the vast folds of the balloon as it expanded in the upper air.

But such a fragile cover! And no net? This was a monstrosity, cried balloon authorities. The balloon was not safe! A German permit for an ascent from Augsburg was refused the "foreign" professor from

Switzerland. However, a Swiss certificate of "airworthiness" was obtained from Berne. It was accepted, and the legal difficulty was overcome.

And now the FNRS was off. The balloon was named for the society which had financed this pioneer ascent, the Belgian National Fund for Scientific Research, (Fonds National Belge de la Recherche Scientifique). The flight was followed by enthusiastic Piccard supporters as well as by skeptical and gloomy predictions of the European press.

Man had been trying to imitate the birds for centuries. There had been balloons and balloons; balloons for pleasure, for carnivals, delightful creations fantastically decorated, carrying up poor patient horses, acrobats, stages. How many fatal plunges to earth, how many fiery disasters in the air, had ended these early attempts to fly! From the first Montgolfier balloon of 1783, there followed a hot-air balloon, with its open basket for passengers, the sight-seeing balloon, and now this—a gas-filled madness.

Never before had a balloon been designed to ascend with safety into upper space where man had never been. In 1862, two balloonists, James A. Glaisher and Henry Coxwell, ascended in an open gondola with the intent of making observations in the stratosphere. But Glaisher fell unconscious from lack of oxygen—at 20,000 feet oxygen is scarce. Coxwell was so frostbitten that he had to use his teeth to open the release valve to descend to earth. Of course, no observations had been possible.

Auguste Piccard, Swiss professor, engineer, physicist, inventor, and perhaps above all, explorer, was being borne aloft into the upper air, his goal an altitude of ten miles, his purpose to record the action of cosmic rays. This flight of the FNRS, an historic pio-

They were rising rapidly past a factory chimney.

neer ascent into the stratosphere, was to have far-reaching effects.

The two aeronauts did not realize at first that the earth had been left behind. Professor Piccard was busy checking his instruments and his pressurized cabin. After the first tug, his airship slipped quietly away like a soaring bird. Looking out one of the three-inch portholes, he saw that they were passing over a factory chimney, and rising.

The Professor had no doubts about his cabin. His calculations took everything into account. His life and Kipfer's depended on the strength and airtight security of the aluminum sphere. The balloon car, or "gondola," made of sheet aluminum one-seventh of an inch thick, measured seven feet in diameter — room enough for two passengers and their various instruments. The eight little portholes were formed of two sheets of glass, separated by a thin layer of air. These windows would not break, even under pressure of nine-tenths of an atmosphere (which is what they would have to sustain). Also, they would not be clouded by frost even in the stratosphere, where the outside temperature drops to 76 degrees below zero.

The cabin, Professor Piccard knew, would be perfectly safe. But what was this? Now, in full flight, Auguste Piccard heard a strange, whistling sound, as of air escaping. It *was* air escaping! Their precious oxygen. The insulator of an electric sounder that passed through the cabin wall had been broken when the cabin was tossed about by the wind. It left a hole through which air was leaking.

The Professor quickly pressed insulating tape around the opening and tried to seal it with a mixture of tow and vaseline. It was a difficult job, because the air kept whistling through. While he was working at it, Kipfer informed him that the pressure inside the cabin was the same as that outside, whereas it should

[15]

have been the same as at ground level. The balloon was two and a half miles up.

Here, at the very beginning of their ascent, were they going to have to let the gas out of the balloon and return to earth? They would suffocate if the cabin was not airtight.

The hole was large, but at last Professor Piccard managed to seal it. The whistling ceased.

The Professor had prepared for almost every conceivable emergency. He had brought along some liquid oxygen. Slowly, carefully, a little at a time, he poured some on the floor. As the oxygen evaporated, the air pressure in the cabin increased. The balloon was going up with amazing rapidity. Twenty-eight minutes earlier they were at Augsburg, 1,850 feet above sea level. Now they had reached an altitude of 51,200 feet. They had risen over nine miles in 28 minutes. The mercury barometer read 2.92 inches; at sea level it is about 30 inches.

They had reached the stratosphere; they were mounting higher and higher within it!

With almost unbelievable speed the FNRS had shot up through the earth's atmosphere and through the troposphere, the height of which on that day proved later to have been seven and a half miles. The gas in the balloon had now expanded fully; under the reduced pressure of the upper atmosphere it was ten times its earth-bound volume. The pear-shaped balloon had swelled to a perfect sphere and now drifted horizontally.

Up in that rarified sphere the sky was poignantly beautiful; deep, dark blue, almost black. Had they been able to see through the troposphere, the balloonists would have had a visual field of more than 280 miles in radius—248,000 square miles of earth—more than all of France.

Beyond them lay the horizon, in a straight line, as though marked off by a ruler. The earth below, however, was concealed by the fogginess of the troposphere. Only by looking straight down could the land itself be viewed. It looked fuzzy, as in a poor photograph. Only the summits of the Bavarian Alps and the Tyrol stood revealed above the clouds.

The balloon would have to rise so as not to rake the tops of those mountains when they descended. "We must throw out the ballast," the Professor said. The ballast, which consisted of 750 bags of small lead-shot, passed through a funnel from the cabin into an outside container fastened to the frame. This container had two compartments, one above the other, each with its separate air-lock. When the top air-lock was closed, the bottom one could be opened and the shot poured out. This "lead sand" as the Professor called it, could harm no one below, for it would spread out over a wide area. Furthermore, the Professor had tested it himself by standing 165 feet beneath a shower of the shot and letting it pour over him.

Now Kipfer pulled the switch releasing the ballast, and a hundred pounds of lead shot dropped earthward. The balloon rose several hundred yards. It was then that the Professor made a disturbing discovery. Somehow the rope that operated the valve which allowed gas to escape from the balloon was fouled. It had become tangled with the restraining rope fastened to the ground-maneuvering belt.

The restraining rope, which was meant to hold the balloon down during the wind at the time of take-off, might prevent their return to earth. If they could not release the gas they would not be able to make a landing when they wanted to. They would be at the mercy of the wind and the temperature. As it grew colder after sunset and the hydrogen gas within the balloon contracted, then and then only would the balloon descend. But where? It might be over the sea; the Adriatic lay just beyond, and they were headed in that direction.

However, they had not yet reached the barometric height necessary to get the records that the Professor sought. More ballast was thrown out. This done, the balloon rose higher. The aeronauts reached the height they were aiming for, but they knew they would have to return to earth without waiting to collect cosmic ray data.

Although the pressure within the cabin was now adjusted, their precarious situation because of the fouled up gas valve was serious. When the temperature became colder and the gas contracted, the balloon would allow the rope to hang lower, and it would then pull on the valve. The valve would open, and as the gas escaped, the balloon would descend rapidly toward earth—perhaps too rapidly, beyond their control.

They must retain some of their remaining ballast until almost the very moment of landing, as was customary. Dumping ballast at the last minute would lighten the balloon and avoid a rough and possibly damaging landing.

"We will pack up our instruments," the Professor said. The men would thus avoid being struck by loose, falling objects, and the instruments, too, would be far safer. Now once more they tried to open the gas valve. A crank inside the cabin was designed to turn a windlass around which the valve cable wound. But when the crank was turned, the cable parted.

The balloon was now out of control—on its own.

Nothing to do but sit, wait, and keep the cabin airtight. A buzzing in their ears warned them that the hole around the insulator was leaking again. Air was escaping rapidly. The vaseline had seeped away through the tow. They had, fortunately, plenty of liquid oxygen, and also alkali, which would absorb the carbon dioxide produced by their breathing.

Professor Piccard had planned to alight about midday, and if the oxygen did not leak, there was enough to last until nightfall. But if the flight were to last longer than planned they might be carried over the Adriatic. Right now they were moving rapidly toward that sea, as indicated by the drift rope which hung 150 feet below the aluminum car.

Professor Piccard had studied every aspect of such an ascension as this. Cause and effect followed immutably one upon the other. He had implicit faith in the laws of nature, but it was not possible to foresee every accident. A sudden awkward movement within the cramped space of the cabin caused a large mercury barometer to break, spilling the silvery metal all over the cabin floor!

Mercury can eat through metal under certain conditions. But the coat of paint covering the aluminum would protect it for the time being. How to remove the mercury was the problem. A vacuum cleaner?

They had no vacuum cleaner. But they did have plenty of vacuum. All around them was the immense near-vacuum of space. In fact, never had a physicist more free vacuum to draw upon. Professor Piccard inserted a little rubber tube into a vent that led to the outside. The other end of the tube he passed over the floor. The mercury and also some water that had condensed on the floor disappeared, sucked up cleanly and spirited away into the stratosphere.

The cabin had become very cold. While rising rapidly at the beginning of their flight, frost had formed on the inside walls of their aluminum sphere. The air inside the cabin grew colder and colder. It was like being inside a huge snow crystal. Fortunately now the sun rose. And there in the stratosphere its radiance was twice as brilliant as at sea level. The frost began to fall off the aluminum walls.

It actually began to snow in the cabin.

From the arctic to the desert! As the car heated, the temperature quickly became almost unbearably warm. It rose to more than 100 degrees. Half the outside of the aluminum sphere had been painted black, and the black, heat-absorbing side was facing the sun. A motor had been provided to rotate the sphere, but the ground wind had broken that, too.

The two passengers became very thirsty. Water condensed from their breath and their bodies had collected under the flooring, but it was an undrinkable mixture of dust, oil, and mercury droplets. Two large bottles of water were to have been put in the cabin, but only one small bottle could be found.

Before long, however, a pleasant discovery was made. Down the shady side of the wall flowed a trickle of fresh distilled water. It was just enough to wet their lips, but it would do until the Professor thought of something better.

To the physicist the laws of nature furnish many answers, many rewards. Into an aluminum goblet Auguste Piccard poured some liquid oxygen. As it evaporated, a heavy layer of frost appeared on the outside of the cup. Formed at -250 degrees, it was too cold to touch. But in a few moments it was reduced to melting ice.

The sun climbed straight overhead, and the cabin hung directly in the shadow of the balloon. The aluminum sphere grew cooler. The heat-absorbing black side swung away from the sun, which also helped to make the cabin cool and comfortable.

Afternoon came; the balloon descended slightly. But at its slow rate of descent, it would take fifteen

The balloon began to descend amidst high mountains.

days to reach the earth. Sitting quietly, conserving their precious oxygen, the balloonists waited. At last they began to drop a little faster. But it would still take 24 hours to reach earth. As the day reached late afternoon, the balloon became much colder, and the gas contracted. They descended quicker and quicker.

The sun went down below the horizon and the balloon was descending more and more rapidly. A serious problem still existed, however. If the valve did not open and if they threw over more ballast than was required to ease the shock of landing, the balloon would again soar ten miles up, back into the stratosphere. They must retain enough ballast to make sure of reaching the earth. Whether the landing were rough or not could not be helped.

As they reached lower altitudes, Piccard and Kipfer carefully let some of the air out of the cabin through an air cock. Anxiously they watched the barometers. Equal pressures outside and inside were at last recorded at 15,000 feet. The portholes could now be opened, and with great relief and delight the two aeronauts thrust their heads out into the open air. They had been shut up in their aluminum cabin for 17 hours. Beneath them stretched snowy peaks and barren rocks. Lightning flashed momentarily from two small clouds, but there was no thunder. They were drifting away from the storm sounds.

They were in the high mountains, headed toward an icy pass to the north. Something was bound to happen at any minute now. The Professor did not dare throw out any more ballast for fear that the balloon would suddenly shoot up once more into the stratosphere—and with the portholes open this would be fatal.

The only way to manage the FNRS and keep it from ascending again would be to entirely empty the balloon of its gas. Auguste Piccard waited, holding the strap that would open the emergency panel in the cover and deflate the balloon instantly.

They were approaching a steep slope, covered with snow. The gondola touched. But the Professor did not pull the strap to release the gas. The site was far too dangerous for a landing. The gondola bounced, and sped lightly over a crevasse-riven glacier. The Professor could see the lights of a village in the valley below, and he signaled toward it with his flashlight. On and on they moved through the night, until finally they hovered over a flat, ice-covered plain that appeared to have no crevasses. Now! Kipfer pulled sharply on the ripping panel, the balloon quickly deflated, the cabin touched the ice, and rolled gently back and forth to a stop.

There was a moment of anxiety as from his porthole Professor Piccard saw that the envelope of the balloon was hovering over their cabin. If it collapsed it might bury them under its monstrous folds. But a light wind luckily swayed the balloon to one side; gently it bowed over and rested upon the glacier—for that was where the FNRS had landed. The ripping panel fortunately lay underneath so that the great balloon emptied very

[24]

The two men were stranded high on an Alpine glacier.

slowly, and lay there like a giant creature breathing its last.

The dark cabin was a welter of overturned instruments, 400 pounds of them. There were also 750 bags of small shot scattered about upside down. Kipfer was struggling out from beneath all this.

The balloonists had landed at an altitude of 8,700

feet, but whether they were in Switzerland or Italy they could not guess. It was bitter cold, there, in the icy splendor of the Alps.

"We'll bivouac here," the Professor said. He and Kipfer crawled under the voluminous folds of the balloon's covering. They slept there on the glacier, disturbed only by dreams and the hissing of leaking oxygen—two intrepid explorers, engineer and scientist, alone in the frigid immensity and magnificence of glacial heights.

A plane sent out to search for the "lost" balloonists spied the FNRS spread out upon the glacier below. The pilot believed the collapsed balloon lying beneath was proof of the death of the Professor and Kipfer. He hastened back to report to the newspapers the disastrous finish of the expedition. But with the approach of dawn, the Professor and Paul Kipfer awoke. They spread out the dark oblong banner which was to have served both for identification and to shade the cabin from the sun, and waited.

When daylight came up over the edge of the world, the two aeronauts tied themselves together with a double rope, and testing the snow at every step—with a length of bamboo taken from the rigging of the balloon—they proceeded down across the glacier. Climbing laboriously over the massive drifts and the outcropping rocks, skidding down cliffsides, they reached the head of the valley below.

It was noon when they were met by a party of skiers, sent out to bring them back to the village of Gurgl, a tiny cluster of houses grouped in an Alpine meadow at the foot of the glacier. A relief squad of twenty soldiers and twenty villagers went on up to the landing place of the FNRS. They rolled the envelope of the balloon into a long sausage-like bundle and carried it back down the glacier on their shoulders.

The cabin was found to be undamaged and it was drawn down over the snow like a sled, and into the proud little village of Gurgl. The Gurgl Glacier was renamed, and today is called Piccard Glacier.

In Zurich, a few days later, the Swiss Aero Club welcomed the aeronauts with honor; there were parades and flowers and speeches. School children waved and shouted. Colonel Messner, the President of the Club, congratulated Professor Piccard, and hoped that "his record would stand for many years."

"To the contrary," said the Professor modestly, revealing the man and the scientist in his reply. "It will be a fine day for me when other stratospheric balloons follow me and reach altitudes greater than I have. My aim is not to maintain records, but to open a new domain to scientific research and to aerial navigation."

And indeed, the results of this gallant enterprise were not at first recognized, because the Professor had been unable to gather his cosmic ray data. The press made much of this failure, characterizing the flight as Professor Piccard's "mad" exploit. One newspaper even announced his death. "Wrapped in silence and shrouded in the folds of night, and helpless before fate," the story stated dramatically, "the Piccard stratosphere

[27]

balloon is floating aimlessly over the glaciers of the Tyrolean Alps, out of control, and occupied only by the dead."

But the Professor was far from dead. Yet such has often been the reception of a new idea or invention. Later the hermetically sealed, air-conditioned cabin was to be recognized as a model, while the light structure of the balloon envelope led directly to further inventions, as well as to the use of unmanned balloons for scientific research.

In spite of his failure, the Professor was not through with the FNRS. The very next year he and the Belgian engineer, Professor Max Cosyns, made another ascent in this same balloon from Zurich. This time everything went according to plan. "You must look after every detail yourself," the Professor always said.

Watching the FNRS on that second ascent was a handsome boy of ten, Jacques Piccard, the Professor's only son. He and his three sisters had been in Zurich for the flight preparations. They had seen a huge canvas spread over a wide, empty flight field, covering brush and stones. They had watched the long, snake-like roll of the balloon carried out of the hangar, to be carefully stretched out upon the protective canvas. They had watched the great dome inflate with gas and rise up like a mammoth mushroom, held back by a hundred spidery cables.

When it was released, the balloon shot with astonishing speed straight up into the air. The field lights illuminated the silvery aluminum cabin; all the rigging and the bottom part of the balloon were etched in light against the dark sky.

Jacques peered up into the sky, waiting until that speck vanished into the blue. Little did he dream that he himself would one day establish a record in another kind of balloon. He could not have imagined that the time would come when he would descend into the uttermost depths of the sea, just as then his father was soaring aloft into the highest region that man had at that time yet reached.

The Professor himself had always hoped to investigate the ocean depths. Now, however, he sought a particular gamma radiation of the cosmic rays which was thought to be extremely active in the stratosphere. On his second ascent in the FNRS he got the information that he was looking for. He found that the gamma radiation was very slight, and often did not exist.

Drifting smoothly over Lake Wallen, over Southern Switzerland, and over the lovely Lake Garda, the FNRS descended at Desenzano, Italy. It had surpassed its earlier altitude record, and to the great satisfaction of all concerned, that record remained with Switzerland. There was a great demonstration in the Italian city; the aeronauts were greeted with cheers and the warmest of welcomes. Not long afterward the Aero Club of Zurich, which had sponsored this flight, received Auguste Piccard royally. The streets of Zurich were lined with cheering crowds, the shining aluminum cabin was paraded on a truck, and the King and Queen of Belgium, who had been Professor Piccard's good friends, were on hand to welcome and congratulate him.

The FNRS, having ascended higher in the stratosphere than on its initial flight, had, according to the barometers, attained 55,800 feet of altitude. Later, however, the altitude was judged by the International Aeronautical Foundation to have been only 53,139 feet. But it is now known that the atmosphere is never in a steady state, and barometric pressure is not an accurate measure of altitude.

After the Zurich flight the fame of the FNRS and its accomplishment was universally acknowledged. The United States, Russia, and Poland at once set about building stratospheric balloons of their own, modeling them after the FNRS. They constructed airtight cabins and used the lightest of balloon envelopes. All of these were larger than the Piccard balloon, and "The Century of Progress" built by the United States eventually set a new world record.

Two years after the Zurich ascent, in August 1934, the FNRS again rose into the air, with Monsieur Cosyns as pilot and Monsieur van der Elst as assistant. They were commissioned to observe the connection between the mountains of Yugoslavia and those of the Ardennes. Once more—and as fate had it, for the last time—the balloon rose into the stratosphere, and returned.

Now the delicate fabric was worn out. The rubberized envelope began to split. The first of the stratospheric balloons could no longer be used as a gas aerostat.

Professor Piccard and Cosyns tried to make a hot-air balloon out of it. As such, it would have moved with the air, warmed by the sun. But this was not to be. The balloon was swept back by the wind over the heating apparatus, and caught fire from the blaze below. In a few minutes it was completely destroyed. This had been the fate of dozens of hot-air balloons in the past.

But Auguste Piccard had proved that the stratospheric balloon had a function. Until such time as instruments could be devised to be sent aloft, the presence of an observer was essential to study the composition of the atmosphere surrounding the planets and other celestial bodies. Meanwhile the scientist-engineer, physicist-inventor, turned his attention to other worlds to explore.

The stratospheric balloon led the way to Piccard's eventual conquest of the depths of the sea. Almost from the beginning Auguste Piccard had dreamed of that goal. He had proven that man could ascend into pressures much less than that of earth's surface in a balloon able to transport cabin, passengers, and instruments. Might not the same means be adapted for descending into the depths of the sea?

There was a direct analogy between the balloon and the deep-sea ship. The free balloon rises as soon as it is released, and descends when the lighter-than-

[31]

air gas is allowed to escape. The deep-sea ship, supported by a lighter-than-water float, would descend with its ballast as the gas was released or diminished, and would rise again when the ballast was dropped.

The deep-sea ship would, like the balloon, require an airtight cabin, one built to resist tremendous pressure. It would be furnished with portholes from which to view the then little-known submarine world.

Auguste Piccard had had this idea ever since he was a first-year student in the Federal Institute of Technology at Zurich. Indeed, the desire to build a deep-sea ship was his first love; the study of cosmic rays had diverted him for the time to a balloon. But the time was to come when the deep-sea ship would be built, when Auguste Piccard and his son Jacques would be the first to descend into the depths of the ocean, where man had never before ventured.

The time was to come when Jacques Piccard would with his own eyes look upon the deepest spot, the lowest valley, in earth's submerged crust. And even before that time both Piccards, father and son, would be greeted as "Admirals of the Abyss."

Chapter 2

A Boy With a Dream

Auguste and Jean Piccard were identical twins. They were born in 1884 in the Swiss city of Bale. They grew up in the rarefied atmosphere of the Swiss Alps in the midst of a scholarly and scientific environment. Their father, Jules Piccard, was a teacher of chemistry at the University of Bale.

Auguste, during his school days, found it most depressing when he had to learn a page of Homer by heart. His whole interest was in science, in the sea and the sky. After completing his studies at Bale, he went to the Federal Institute of Technology in Zurich. By then he was already "a passionate research engineer."

He earned a diploma in mechanical engineering in 1910, and three years later was honored with the title "Doctor of Sciences." He was elevated from assistant professor to full professor at Zurich. In 1932 he left Switzerland to take over the professorship of physics on the faculty of Applied Sciences at the Brussels Free University.

Auguste Piccard has written over 200 scientific papers in addition to having invented and constructed two very remarkable "ships" for which he has gained world fame — his airship and the bathyscaphe. Great strides were made in science during the first of the twentieth century, and Auguste, then but a young lad, thrilled with each new bit of knowledge, particularly anything that had to do with the sea.

In the years between, Auguste married. His wife was Marianne Denis, the daughter of a distinguished historian of the Paris Sorbonne. Professor Denis had worked with President Masaryk in drawing up the Lansing declaration of sympathy with the cause of Yugoslav independence in 1918. Marianne herself was an ardent student of history. And then came the young Piccards, Denis, Jacques, Marianne, Helene, and six years later Genevieve joined them — the cadette of the family, as the Swiss French say. Four daughters and one son.

All this time technology had been striding forward. Dr. William Beebe, the distinguished American naturalist, devised a "bathysphere" in which he could descend into the sea. In June, 1930, he was lowered in this steel ball into the tropical waters off Bermuda. Beebe had already made hundreds of dives in a type of diving bell that rested on his shoulders and was supplied with fresh air by a pressure pump.

So enthusiastic was Beebe about the marvelous sights of the underwater world that he begged his friends to "beg, borrow, or steal some kind of helmet" so that they, too, might see its wonders. He had descended only 65 feet at that time; what would he see were he able to dive still further down?

Diving off Haiti one day Dr. Beebe realized that he was observing a world of life "almost as unknown as that of Mars or Venus." So enthralled was he with what he saw that he began at once to plan a submarine sphere, inside of which he could descend with safety to much greater depths.

The idea of a bathysphere was not entirely new. In 1899 an Italian, Piatti Dal Pozzo, had built a steel sphere ten feet in diameter, which could be lowered 160 feet. But without other air supply than it carried within, it could not go deeper; nor could it remain submerged for long. However, by uniting this idea with plans for an airhose, and portholes, Beebe designed a sphere which could go down deeper.

The result was the bathysphere. The engineering details were worked out by Dr. Beebe's companion, Otis Barton. The day came when the two men were bolted inside their steel observation laboratory for its descent. Through the crystal porthole of the bathysphere they saw forms of almost unbelievable beauty and wonder, shapes of extravagant ferocity and variety, moving freely in the black night of their native element.

Luminous flashes starred the depths, constellations of "living light." There were beautiful and complicated jellyfish, unknown organisms, transparent, glowing green or red, expanding and contracting as they flowed by the crystal window of the metal sphere, their tentacles streaming out like fluted ribbons. Most of these creatures had never been captured by trawls, and many forms were quite unknown to Dr. Beebe. He was enchanted, as was the world, by these glimpses of ocean life.

The Beebe bathysphere, although it made a record dive for that time, had been able to descend to a depth of only 2,510 feet. And although this remarkable sphere had at last furnished the means of viewing depths so long hidden from man, it had certain very dangerous disadvantages.

Hanging by a cable from a "mother" ship, it was actually an underwater prison which, were its cable severed, would become a sealed tomb. Also it was small—only four feet and nine inches in diameter, and rather tiresomely crowded for a tall man. It could not move by itself, and if the mother vessel above were rocked by the waves, the bathysphere was subjected to dangerous jolting.

Professor Piccard was vitally interested in the bathysphere, but *his* deep-sea sphere must be independent; it must be able to dive and ascend by itself. It must be so constructed that it would withstand the great pressures of the abyssal depths. (Several years after the first plunge of the bathysphere, Otis Barton built a "benthosphere" in which he made a record descent of 4,462 feet. He reported that the world "down below" was "dazzling, unbelievable.")

But at the time Dr. Beebe made his record dive, Auguste Piccard was not yet ready to go ahead with plans for his own deep-sea boat. Other scientific studies were at that time more demanding. He was then concerned with the effects of cosmic rays. Were they greatly diminished in their passage through earth's atmosphere? Could they not be better studied above the earth, beyond the clouds?

As his study of cosmic rays progressed Auguste Piccard came upon more and more questions which only stratospheric observation could answer. He would build a stratospheric balloon and see for himself.

But the air authorities shook their heads. No one had ever done it. Nevertheless he began at once to plan a balloon. He went to the Belgian National Society for Scientific Research, which had just been founded by King Albert of Belgium, and it was from them that he got the funds for the FNRS.

When Professor Auguste Piccard had proved indisputably that he could build a balloon which would bear man up into the stratosphere he knew that he could also build a deep-sea boat. A bathyscaphe to take man into the abyssal depths could be designed on the same principle as the stratospheric balloon.

In 1934, when Jacques was a leggy boy of twelve,

the Professor designed and built a new house for his family at Chexbres, not far from Lausanne on Lake Leman. No lovelier site could be imagined. The little town clustered on a terraced hillside overlooking the blue lake; opposite it were the snowy Alps, wreathed in mist and lacy cloud, and reflected in the satiny waters of the lake. It was as beautiful a spot as could be found in all Switzerland.

The Piccard chateau looked down upon the lake and across to the toothed peaks that seemed to rise from the depths of the lake. Vineyards covered the steep slopes, and tiled roofs nestled among the trees. Here and there a steeple or tall chimney rose above the trees.

The house was long and roomy, three stories high with a basement floor beneath. It had shiny oaken floors, wide halls and staircases, and handsome, sturdy furniture. It was an ideal place for five children to grow up in; free and uncluttered, filled with young people and with friends. There were long, awninged balconies, a spring-fed swimming pool at the foot of the terrace, and a tennis court behind the house. The Professor planted cedar hedges and splendid pines, and he terraced the slopes.

Yes, it was an ideal place in which to grow up, with an elementary school not far down the road, a strict school where the teacher did not hesitate to rap knuckles sharply.

From both his parents Jacques and his four sisters learned the habits of precision and industry that are second nature to the Piccards. There was always music in the family, from a piano, flute, guitar; and talk of balloons and physics. The Piccards were a close-knit family of warm affections, of merriment, of strict religious faith, economy, and efficiency.

From such a boyhood the young Jacques, growing like a beanpole through his teens, absorbed from both parents the history of the free Swiss—in which his forbears had taken part—and he absorbed also from his father much of the philosophy of science. The details of a balloon ascension became as clear to Jacques as a good game of tennis. There was always an exceptionally close bond between Jacques and his father, yet never was the boy pressured to follow his father's career.

Auguste Piccard's opportunity to build a deep-sea ship came suddenly and unexpectedly. At an official reception in Brussels, he was asked by King Leopold of Belgium, who had been so intensely interested in the stratospheric balloon, what he was doing at the time.

"Your Majesty," replied the Professor impulsively—he had not considered speaking of the dream of his life at this time—"I am planning to build a deep-sea research submarine, a bathyscaphe, or deep boat, for diving to the bottom of the sea."

There followed a stream of questions and answers, and at last the Professor found he had definitely committed himself to this long-thought-of project. "We

[41]

have no choice now but to do it," he told his laboratory assistants the following day. "I told the King yesterday that we are going to build a bathyscaphe."

The Director of the Fonds National thought it was a wonderful idea, but did not believe that the various advisory committees would agree to such a novel

"I merely want your opinion," the Professor said.

undertaking. However, scientist, engineer, inventor though he was, Auguste Piccard was also a diplomat.

He went first to the Committee for Natural Sciences. "I am not asking you for money for this project," he at once disarmed them. "I merely want to ask your opinion."

Did they think that it would be of interest to natural science to have a small submarine descend to the very bottom of the ocean, with windows through which abyssal life could be observed?

The answer, of course, was emphatically "Yes."

Now for the FNRS Technical Committee. He did not ask their opinion of the scientific merit of his plan (that had already been confirmed), nor did he ask for financial aid. He wanted to know if, in their opinion, a submarine could be built that could descend 13,000 feet.

There was hemming and hawing, for the engineers did not like to have to commit themselves. Finally, however, the consensus was: "Frankly, we doubt that the construction of such a craft is possible, but if Professor Piccard says it can be built, it can be. We have full confidence in his ability."

There remained only the Finance Committee. He made himself quite clear to them. He was not asking them to pass upon the scientific value of a bathyscaphe, nor on the engineering feasibility. These factors had already been determined. All he asked was:

"Can you find the money to support the project?"

They could. Some $25,000, or one million pre-war Belgian francs, were granted. It was 1937 when work on the bathyscaphe began in earnest at the Brussels Free University.

High-pressure testing equipment was built. Test followed test of mockups, models, portholes, cabins, and floats. It took two years for the general outline of the project to become clear. In all the experiments,

[43]

Professor Piccard was aided by his young assistant, Jean Guillissen. Jacques was, at this time, studying at the University of Geneva.

And then, in 1939, World War II broke out. All Europe was in its dreadful throes. Young Jean Guillissen lost his life in the war. Professor Piccard was recalled from Brussels to his native country.

In 1944, Jacques, now even taller than his father, dark-haired and dark-eyed like his French mother, enlisted in the French army. He was twenty-two and the love of freedom was his heritage. He returned two years later with sergeant's stripes and a Croix de Guerre. At long last the Armistice brought some peace to the world.

After the war Jacques returned to Geneva to complete his university courses. The Professor, however, remained in Switzerland until 1954, the last year of his teaching assignment there. Once more Auguste Piccard's mind turned toward his bathyscaphe. Would the Belgian "Fonds National" still be interested? He went to Brussels to find out.

Yes, "Fonds National" was still interested in the project, but prices were not what they had been before the war. It would now cost almost twice as much to build the bathyscaphe.

Very well, they would have to pare down the cost, even though it meant sacrificing certain features which he had planned.

The Professor's method of arriving at a final design was to list every requirement that must be fulfilled.

One by one he would consider every disadvantage that could lie in each possible solution. Every possible method of construction was carefully examined, and one by one the faulty ones were discarded, until at last the correct answer to all the requirements remained, "fool-proof" and workable.

Now with the bathyscaphe, he considered all the essential features of a deep-sea craft. He listed the various means of meeting these requirements. Was there a flaw here, a structural weakness there? He anticipated every possible need, every unexpected contingency. How well he planned, the world was to learn.

Step by step, he arrived at the basic design of his "deepboat." He knew it must have an airtight cabin just as his FNRS had. Should it be equal in weight to the weight of the water that it displaced? If so it would be in equilibrium, according to the ancient law of Archimedes.

The submarine is built on the principle of equilibrium. But the submarine can dive at best not more than a thousand feet. It is not possible to give the hull of the submarine the thickness and resistance it would need in order to withstand the tremendous pressures of the abyss.

The hull of the bathyscaphe cabin would have to be thicker than the hull of a submarine; therefore it would be heavier than the water it displaced. Being heavier than the water, the hull, or cabin, must be supported by a cable from a surface vessel, as Beebe's bathysphere was, or it must have its own buoyant float.

A boat suspended by a cable would have no freedom of movement, and there was always the danger of the cable breaking. But a float, filled with a substance lighter than water, would permit the heavy steel cabin to go up and down freely.

Now, with the basic idea established, work on the deep-sea boat began in earnest. The Professor made scale models and tested them in tanks under a pressure of 1,600 atmospheres, a pressure equal to the weight of a column of water ten miles high. Problem after problem arose, was studied, and solved.

There was, for example, the question of what was the best thing to fill the float with. The Professor considered many substances, but rejected them all in favor of gasoline, a fluid that was not too light nor too compressible.

He decided to put vent holes at the bottom of the float to form a passage through which sea water could enter or flow out freely, as the gasoline expanded or contracted with changing temperature. Thus the same pressure would always be maintained both inside and outside the float. As the gasoline contracted, water could enter the float; when the gasoline expanded, it would force the water out. Since the pressure inside and outside the float would always be the same, the float could be made of fairly light metal sheeting.

As the bathyscaphe descended into cold water, the gasoline would contract, water would enter, and the float would become heavier. When this happened, ballast could be dropped to lighten the bathyscaphe. The ballast would be stored outside the cabin and could be released by the pilot when necessary. The inventor solved the problem of releasing ballast by having an electromagnet hold it fast. When the current was cut off, the heavy pig iron would drop to the bottom of the sea.

The next thing that had to be determined was how much ballast would be needed under the various conditions of pressure and temperature under the sea. This was carefully calculated.

The cabin must be completely round, since a sphere was the form that could best withstand the great pressures of the ocean depths. And there must be room enough for two persons, the pilot and an observer.

The cigar-shaped float must be large enough to support this cabin. Many experiments in the choice of materials for the actual cabin were made. The Professor had a series of scale models built. They were placed in tanks and subjected to pressures that the real cabin would have to sustain. Many of the models collapsed!

In the end, steel was chosen; steel of the best quality, with a thickness of 3.54 inches reinforced to 5.91 inches around all the openings, the windows, the entrance shaft, the cables and electrical devices. The Professor decided on an inside diameter of 6 and 3/5 feet. The final cabin was cast in two hemispheres and was then tested by radiographic examination for flaws in the steel. In the few spots where flaws were found,

[47]

cones of the weakened material were taken out and replaced by other cones cast to fit. These replacements were set in with the narrow ends turned inward. The entire sphere was then highly polished both inside and out.

A great deal of experimenting was done on the windows. It was found that glass would not do, as it invariably cracked under pressure. But Plexiglas was now being made, and the Professor found that it answered every requirement perfectly. As it was plastic, its elasticity allowed it to adjust to the expansion and contraction of changes in temperature.

These windows were a triumph. They were nearly six inches thick, but beautifully clear, with the transparency of pure crystal. Inside the cabin the windows were nearly four inches in diameter, wide enough for both eyes to see through, and on the outside they widened to 15.75 inches, affording a wide field of vision.

All the joints of this first deep-sea boat were sealed with exquisite care. The joints of the cabin, smoothly and flawlessly machined, were made completely watertight by strong rubber bands which the pressure of the water forced tightly against the metal.

All of these major details, and innumerable smaller ones, each of particular importance, had been taken into account. At last the bathyscaphe, christened with the name *FNRS 2*, was ready to be transported to the site of its first trial dive. It had been decided that Dakar, Africa, would be the port from which the first

A great crane hoisted the bathyscaphe aboard the Scaldis.

descent into the sea would be made.

The Belgian government had placed the cargo
ship *Scaldis* at the disposal of Professor Piccard and
Professor Max Cosyns, to carry the *FNRS 2* and its
staff to Dakar. The bathyscaphe would travel in the
ship's hold, her first journey being *over* the sea, and

neither upon it nor in it. How would she behave when she entered the water?

Of her behavior Professor Piccard had no doubts whatsoever. He was a physicist, and he relied on the laws of nature. No one could have been calmer, more confident. His calculations could not be wrong. His unperturbed certainty inspired confidence.

Enthusiastic friends came down to the port of Antwerp to see the scientist and his deep-sea boat off on their unique adventure. The *Scaldis* passed through the Kruisschans lock and set sail for the open sea. Well wishers waved them farewell, and there was much excitement in the press.

But after all, the *FNRS 2* had never touched water. Would she float? Would she sink never to rise? Would she actually be able to dive deep into the sea—and return?

Chapter 3

The Bathyscaphe Dives

Just off the port of Dakar the French Navy sloop, *Elie Monnier,* gleaming white in a fresh coat of paint, awaited the *Scaldis* and the bathyscaphe party. The *Elie Monnier* was assigned to assist the French Underseas Research Group, which was to take part in the bathyscaphe trials. This same ship had been used as a base by the famous French divers, Jacques Yves Cousteau and Phillippe Tailliez.

Wearing diving suits, the two divers had been taking undersea films—films which were soon to enchant the world. Cousteau had been named as "sea expert" for the bathyscaphe expedition, and he was thrilled at the invitation to make a dive in the deep-sea craft.

The French Underseas Research Group had spent

months preparing for this event, constructing apparatus designed by Professor Piccard. They had made an incredible undersea gun. They had welded a camera mount on the underwater prow of the *Elie Monnier* in order to take automatic undersea films. Special sound equipment also had been installed in the *Elie Monnier* in order to locate the bathyscaphe as she surfaced after a dive.

Cousteau could not wait to see the bathyscaphe. With all speed he lowered a launch to meet the *Scaldis* and climbed aboard. There she lay in the hold, the wonderful bathyscaphe, a metal balloon and an orange-and-white observation car. Electric motors on each side of the float could propel the deep-sea boat under a pressure 400 times greater than that of the surface of the sea.

To reach these great depths, the bathyscaphe needed large quantities of additional weight. This weight consisted of tons of iron ballast held to the bottom of the float by electromagnets. If the bathyscaphe were sinking too fast, some of the ballast could be released. Releasing the ballast made the bathyscaphe lighter and reduced its downward speed. But, if more speed were desired, two air compartments — one located at each end of the float — could be emptied of air and filled with sea water to weigh the bathyscaphe down. If still more weight were needed, some of the gasoline could be released from the gasoline compartments and replaced with the heavier sea water.

[54]

A device that the Professor provided to ease the shock of landing was a 300-pound weight dangling on a cable from the bottom of the cabin. When the bathyscaphe neared the bottom, the weight came to rest on the sea floor first and, in effect, reduced the bathyscaphe's weight by 300 pounds.

The weight-and-cable arrangement also made it easy for the bathyscaphe to hover over the ocean floor and to cruise slowly along.

The bathyscaphe could cruise within a range of about ten miles, and its speed was slow enough to offer observers plenty of time to check and recheck any interesting features they encountered on the ocean floor.

The observation car had been designed to withstand pressures encountered at 50,000 feet — although there is no such sea depth anywhere in the world. Anyway, it was not planned to descend more than 13,000 feet during the test dives, but even this depth would be twelve times as deep as any submarine could go then.

The first descent of the *FNRS 2* was to take place off the lee side of the island of Bao Vista, one of the Cape Verde Islands. On October 19, 1948, the *Scaldis*, attended by the French Navy contingent, steamed out of Dakar's harbor to the scene of the first dive.

The three divers, Cousteau, Tailliez, and Dumas, had charge of adding gasoline and ballast to the deep-sea craft, and would also track it under water. After the dive they would recover it and tow it safely back to the *Scaldis*.

[55]

Having arrived off Bao Vista, the bathyscaphe had to be unloaded from the hold of the *Scaldis*. A great crane lifted her up over the rail, then lowered her gently down to the water. Now for the first time the boat which was to conquer the depths, touched the surface of the sea. She floated proudly on the swells, riding high because the tanks in her float were still filled only with air.

Eager eyes watched her from the decks of the attending vessels. The bathyscaphe sank slowly until a third of the float was submerged. Now hoses were attached and the float filled with gasoline. To avoid an explosion while the gasoline was being pumped in, the float had been filled with carbon dioxide. This carbon dioxide was drawn off by one hose, and back into the *Scaldis'* tanks, as the gasoline was pumped in to take its place. When the 7,040 gallons were transferred, the float was almost totally submerged beneath the surface of the sea.

Leaning over the rail and watching each operation with a keen and affectionate eye, the Professor experienced the warm satisfaction of a creator whose calculations have proven right.

The bathyscaphe was now loaded with its ballast under the direction of Jacques Piccard. The *FNRS 2* sank out of sight on its maiden dive. After the craft reached a pre-set depth, an automatic pilot released the ballast, and the bathyscaphe rose. The unmanned test had been successful.

The deep-sea boat was emptied of gasoline and

The Professor watched closely as the FNRS 2 was made ready.

hoisted once more up into the ship's hold. They were ready for the manned dive. The *Elie Monnier* set out to take depth soundings at different points. A place was selected where the bottom sloped gently downward. There on October 21 the two ships dropped anchor in a hundred feet of water.

It took five arduous days to prepare the bathyscaphe for her manned dive. The final job was to attach the 1,200 pound battery and the tons of iron pigs that were to be held in place by the electromagnets.

Inside the cabin was a dazzling array of implements, gages, indicators, and the most perfect oxygen generator and air purifier that had ever been built. Two passengers could remain within the sphere for twenty-four hours without discomfort or danger. The outside flood lamps were strong enough for color pictures to be taken, even in the blackness of the depths.

One of the bathyscaphe's important features was an automatic pilot which could release the ballast when the deep-sea boat reached a predetermined depth. There was also a time switch which would release the ballast in case the bathyscaphe came to rest on a ledge before it had reached the desired depth.

For the first manned descent the automatic pilot would not be used, and it was not supposed to be connected. Professor Cosyns, however, *had* connected it, although he did not wind the time switch. Professor Piccard, on entering the cabin, and observing the silent clock, had, like a true clock-concious Swiss, wound it!

As a result, while the bathyscaphe was still in the hold of the *Scaldis,* one of the batteries which controlled a part of the ballast, suddenly released the load. Tons of metal crashed into the hold. Fortunately, no one was standing beneath the iron shower.

This accident caused a day's delay, but Professor Piccard consoled himself with the knowledge that the robot pilot worked.

The great day came at last, a day for the test which

[58]

Professor Piccard was "rejoicing to be able to carry out at last." All the complicated workings of the *FNRS 2* would be put to actual test. Cosyns, as engineer, chose to remain at the surface. Professors Monod and Piccard descended into the hold of the *Scaldis*, entered the manhole atop the float of the bathyscaphe, and slid down into the cabin. Good wishes followed them. "A bientot! Bonne chance." It was just three in the afternoon of October 26. The heavy door to the manhole was lowered by cable, put into place and bolted shut, sealing the two professors within.

The bathyscaphe began to rise from the hold of the *Scaldis*. It was lifted up, and over the rail. Through the portholes the professors could see the ocean rising to meet them. The water rose over the portholes, and the cabin was suffused with a beautiful blue light. They were on their way. But no! The windows emerged from the water again. What had happened? If the test were to fail, deep diving would be set back probably for years.

The telephone was not working because it had not been connected. Too many cooks spoil the broth. They sank again, but only a fathom's depth. The pumps started; gasoline was passing from the *Scaldis* into the tanks in the float. They descended slowly and a swimmer appeared before the portholes, a diver from the *Elie Monnier* wearing goggles and feet flippers. The cabin was unlighted, so Professor Piccard lit up his own face with a flashlight so that the diver could see him.

Above them the tropical night was falling rapidly and the lights of the *Scaldis* lit up the sea, but still the bathyscaphe did not descend. Professor Piccard turned on the cabin lights, and the watchers above saw the ocean glow. There was nothing the two scientists could do but wait. A second diver discovered them quietly playing chess in the tiny cabin. Knocking on the walls, he attracted their attention and held up a board on which was written: "You are going down. Don't stay there too long. Don't start anything working."

What did this message mean? Were the crew putting the ballast aboard? And why must they not start up the motor? The designer of the bathyscaphe wanted to see the propellers working! But they must have been descending swiftly all the time, for suddenly Dr. Monod exclaimed, "We're on the bottom!" Gently, without a single bump, they had landed, after having dived fourteen fathoms. The lights of the *Scaldis* shone down through the water illuminating a vast area even at 84 feet below the surface.

But where were the wonders of the sea bottom they had expected to see? A flat empty stretch of gray silt rippled away out of sight. No coral, no anemones, nothing but a few dark patches. A lone fish swam by, glowing with a greenish phosphorescence. "It was not the cold living light of the sea," Dr. Monod said, "but a luminescent algae with which the fish was covered."

The time came to return to the surface. Professor Piccard pressed a button, and through the window he could see a tub of iron scrap drop away. Another button was pushed, and another tub of ballast fell. The bathyscaphe began to rise. Luminous flashes glowed outside the window, like distant stars.

At ten o'clock their float broke the surface. The winch of the *Scaldis* began lifting them out of the sea. When presently a porthole emerged from the water the professors could see the entire crew standing at the rail of the *Scaldis*, the Professor's son Jacques towering head and shoulders above the rest. Little did either of them guess that only five years later Jacques would be going down, many fathoms deeper, in another bathyscaphe.

The *FNRS 2* had functioned perfectly on this test dive. The same apparatus which had furnished the first *FNRS* with fresh oxygen during the seventeen hours spent in the stratosphere had kept the air fresh fourteen fathoms down. They would go on with the diving. They had seen no wonderful sights at the ocean bottom on this maiden descent, but from the standpoint of achievement, it was thrilling.

A sleeping volcano loomed skyward from the little island of Fogo in the Cape Verde Islands. The last eruption had left great paths of slick lava reaching from the crest down to the sea, yet in spite of this warning, the coast was rimmed with little villages. Within the shelter of El Fogo, the *FNRS 2* would make its second unmanned dive.

[61]

There was one rule that was clearly understood; there would be successive unmanned dives, but the bathyscaphe would not make a descent with a crew "to more than two-thirds of the greatest depth previously reached without a crew." This rule would provide a margin of safety.

So the *FNRS 2* was to be sent down alone to 825 fathoms. An antenna hung below the bathyscaphe would cause the ballast to be released when the antenna touched the bottom. The rolling of the *Scaldis* caused the antenna to be bumped while the *FNRS 2* was still on the surface, and at once tons of ballast fell into the water. The dive was off for that day.

Three days later, the *Scaldis* and the *Elie Monnier* steamed into a glassy little bay behind the island of Sao Thiago, where the sea was deeper and conditions were ideal for another try. The automatic pilot was set for 770 fathoms, the time switch for 4:40 p.m. It was already rather late in the morning but it was decided that there would still be plenty of time for the bathyscaphe to descend and return. However, it was one o'clock before the submarine craft could be launched. But whether tide or current had carried them away from their position, they found, when the *Elie Monnier* took new soundings, that there was a depth of only 495 fathoms and that they must tow the *FNRS 2* to deeper waters.

Time was passing. A tow line from the *Scaldis* broke. The *FNRS 2* drifted off. A new cable had to be brought and attached. It was four o'clock when the bathyscaphe at last descended.

The Captain of the *Scaldis* looked over the rail and said gloomily, "During the War, I saw several ships go down exactly as the *FNRS* is going down now. Not one came to the surface again."

"But this is a bathyscaphe," replied Professor Piccard, "and not like any other ship."

Nevertheless he confessed afterward that he had been fearful of the short time remaining for the dive. He never had any doubts about the automatic pilot, or about any of his calculations. The laws of nature could not fail. But was forty minutes enough for the bathyscaphe to go down as far as they wished her to go?

He was not afraid that she could not come up. He was afraid that she would come up too soon.

Everyone was watching; the masts and rigging of the *Elie Monnier* and the *Scaldis* were crowded with crew and visitors. Several small boats from both frigates were dotted about the bay, waiting, waiting. Auguste Piccard, too, was waiting—for an orange float to break the surface. Some distance away he could just see what looked like a small boat. . . .

Yes, it was the *FNRS 2*! The time was 4:29. It did not seem possible that the bathyscaphe had covered a vertical course of one and three-fifth miles and back in 29 minutes. Could a leak have flooded the cabin and caused the automatic timer to go off? Frogmen from the *Elie Monnier* dived down and reported that they could see drops of water inside one of the portholes. Discouraging; yet it would take only a few drops to dampen a window. The Professor would not give up hope. The wind was rising and when the bathyscaphe was brought alongside the *Scaldis,* it was already dark and the sea was rough. The men could not connect the big hose to drain the gasoline back into the *Scaldis;* the hose was too heavy and the waves were too rough.

To make matters worse these were shark-infested waters, and at that very moment a shark was circling around the float of the bathyscaphe. Seamen could hardly keep their footing on the deck of the float. The Professor ordered the men back to the *Scaldis,* and the corvette set out to tow the bathyscaphe, gasoline and all, back toward the shelter of Santa Clara Bay.

The light float of the *FNRS 2* was not built for waves, and she was being smashed by tons of water. The thin plates of the float breathed in and out. It was a horrible ordeal. If the bathyscaphe got any heavier she would sink, and everything would be lost! They must drain off the gasoline and replace it with the carbon dioxide.

But as it was impossible to connect the heavy gasoline hose, they would have to force the carbon dioxide into the float tube, and simply let the gasoline drain away into the sea.

The loss of the precious gasoline would mean the end of this expedition. But better lose the gasoline than the bathyscaphe. The order went out—no smoking, and no fires. In a few moments the costly fluid was spurting out like a volcano, spraying the faces of the divers and spreading over the waves. Sparks from the funnel of the *Elie Monnier* drifted down; she was hailed with shouts, and ordered to draw away.

Slowly the *Scaldis* battled waves and current, drawing the little deep-sea boat precariously after her, back to the island from which they had so hopefully set out that morning. It was a tense, heart-breaking night. It was presumed that the bathyscaphe was a total wreck, battered by the waves until its plates buckled. At midnight Professor Piccard asked the Captain how far they had come.

"We are still in the same place," the Captain replied grimly. Indeed, they were barely holding their own against the current.

But gradually some headway was made, and by dawn they reached the quiet waters of the bay. The *FNRS 2,* for all her buffeting by the heavy seas, proved to be unhurt. When the hatch was opened, only a little water was found in the cabin, not enough to have set off the automatic pilot causing it to unballast.

Professor Piccard was the first one down inside. One look at the depth recorder showed that the sturdy little ship had actually reached a depth of 759 fathoms.

In 29 minutes the bathyscaphe had traversed 1,518 fathoms, moving at an average rate of five feet a second. It had ascended too swiftly, at more than six feet, six inches a second. This was above what is called the "critical velocity," beyond which the bathyscaphe should not go. It must have rocked violently as it zigzagged upward.

But most important, the cabin itself had returned undamaged to the surface. The principle of the bathyscaphe had been proven sound.

Watching every maneuver of the *FNRS 2* from the deck of the *Elie Monnier,* Yves Cousteau, his dark eyes intent, his lean face alert, saw and appreciated what had happened. "Professor," he shouted, "your invention is the most wonderful of the century."

Chapter 4

Troubled Waters

"After an instant in the headlines, the strange submersible . . . slipped into oblivion." So wrote a French paper following the expedition of the bathyscaphe to Dakar.

So, this was all that the French press had to say — and after what had actually been a successful demonstration of the *FNRS 2*! But alas, new inventions always appear to be met with skepticism and rejection. How many trials and failures did the Wright brothers have before their "flying machine" was taken seriously?

So it was with the bathyscaphe. Those who bade enthusiastic adieu to the Piccards when they left for Antwerp to embark on the *Scaldis* for Dakar, now criticized them for "having attracted world-wide attention in a venture that was obviously doomed to failure."

Actually the descent off Dakar had been invaluable experience. It had shown the Piccards what was needed for the betterment of another bathyscaphe. Professor Piccard returned to Lausanne, and Jacques to Geneva, where he was an assistant in the Faculty of Economic Sciences at the University of Geneva. Neither he nor his father had forgotten, or could forget, the bathyscaphe.

The Belgian Fonds National in the spring of 1949 finally proposed that the French Navy accept the *FNRS 2* and rebuild it at its own expense. This offer was deliberated by the French for the rest of that year. Since the Fonds National usually placed an invention in the hands of the scientist who had built it, Jacques suggested that the *FNRS 2* be shipped to Switzerland. He would try to raise funds to make the changes and repairs that were necessary. Jacques had been assured by many Swiss scientists that they would gladly raise money for the needed improvements in the bathyscaphe.

Jacques felt that under his father's supervision a new float could be built at Toulon, and with the aid of the French Navy, new descents could be made from that port. In this way the French Navy would be put to little expense, the Fonds National would be relieved of any additional charge, and his father would have complete responsibility. This idea seemed to please everyone.

[70]

But—they must wait!

Wait, wait! Back and forth, back and forth, from Switzerland to Paris, to Brussels, to Toulon, went Professor Piccard and his son. Nothing was happening!

Meanwhile, however, something *was* happening in Switzerland. The universities, the institutes, the cantonal governments themselves, as well as many industrialists and private citizens, began to come forward with support. In the spring of 1950 "Secheron," a large industrial plant in Geneva, began work on Professor Piccard's plans for the new bathyscaphe float. An oil company promised 25,000 gallons of gasoline when it should be needed.

Still there was no word from Paris—from the French, who had always played the role of patrons of the arts and sciences! Courteously from the splendid government building on the Place de La Concorde they deferred and deferred, and finally withdrew entirely from any plans for the bathyscaphe.

Then Fonds National came forward with another proposal. They offered to give the *FNRS 2* to the French Navy, together with ample funds to recondition it, provided the French would agree to take full responsibility for the bathyscaphe program. The French, in turn, requested the Piccards to buy ballast for the bathyscaphe. As Jacques drily observed, the shot would be dropped into the sea at each dive, leaving no part of the deep-sea boat in which the Piccards would have a financial interest—the Professor had only invented it!

Three months later an agreement was at last reached. The French accepted the *FNRS 2* and nine million francs from the Fonds National. The *FNRS 2* would be called the *FNRS 3* and Professor Piccard would be asked to act as scientific consultant.

So, the bathyscaphe would dive again! Perhaps within a few months.

But, alas, there was more confusion and delay. It seemed that some French officials thought of the bathyscaphe as simply a different type of submarine, not as an under-sea laboratory and observatory, which was what Professor Piccard had in mind when he designed it. What did a Swiss mountaineer know about a submarine, they asked. Ah, yes, granted he was a genius, but also impractical.

Extracting all the help they could from Auguste Piccard, the French officials then proceeded to ignore him. Nevertheless the kindly inventor-scientist went on furnishing answers to their problems — anything to bring the *FNRS 3* to a successful completion. The plans, the cabin, the float, the implements, had all been his contributions to science.

But fate was working for the Piccards, as it often does when one goes forward to meet it. During this same winter of 1951-52, Jacques Piccard had occasion to go to Trieste. He was preparing a thesis for the Geneva University on the economic possibilities of the Free Territory of Trieste. In that delightful and historic city which from the beginning of its history had been under nine different flags, he met a distinguished historian, Professor de Henriquez, Director of the Museum of War and History.

Professor de Henriquez proposed to Jacques that a new bathyscaphe be built there, in Trieste. Eager to develop the economy and importance of the ancient city, he stressed the advantages of that place. This was a beginning. Other people in Trieste were quick to respond. In no time at all (considering the previous delays elsewhere) the Cantieri Riuniti dell' Adriatico arranged to construct a float. Another cabin of the same dimensions as the first was to be forged at Terni by the Industrial and Electrical Company; it would be a stronger cabin than the *FNRS 3*, for it would be forged, not cast.

Everyone was enthusiastic and delighted. The Italian Navy promised to furnish tugs and escort ships for descents into the Tyrrhenian Sea, and to cap all this, an Italian petroleum company promised to give a tank car of gasoline for the float.

Professor Piccard went to Trieste, the first time he had been in Italy since the balloon descent 20 years before. Work began at once with renewed hope and enthusiasm. Although the budget was barely enough to cover construction, the Piccards, aided by expert craftsmen, constructed the new bathyscaphe and included every safety feature. She would be called the *Trieste,* a name that would go down in history.

The city of Trieste had been prominent in the development of submarines, and because of the presence there of experienced workmen, the new *Trieste* emerged finished, gleaming and impressive, in only fifteen months.

Unlike the *FNRS 3*, the float of the *Trieste* was in the form of a cylinder. It was stronger than the first float, and could be towed at a speed of eight knots. It could also withstand thirty-foot waves.

Professor Piccard calculated that the bathyscaphe would probably "be crushed at about nine or ten miles." Trial dives with an empty bathyscaphe would determine the actual strength of the cabin.

How far could the *Trieste* go after a number of successful empty dives? This would depend mainly on the crew. How deep would they be willing to go? To go further than 3 3/4 miles safely, a heavier and stronger cabin would have to be built. The float would have to be correspondingly larger.

To keep the air fresh in the cabin for the time the crew would be inside, there was an installation that restored oxygen to the air and purified it.

"The human body consumes oxygen and gives out carbon dioxide and water vapor, as you know" Professor Piccard pointed out. "At the same time the lungs release small quantities of organic matter called anthropotoxins. These can be absorbed by means of active carbon."

The equipment would supply oxygen for three persons without difficulty. Indeed, it would furnish more oxygen than two people would need; this excess would have to be stored, shut off, and the air sent through purifying alkaline cartridges. Air purifying

[74]

equipment was no longer unfamiliar, but in the bathyscaphe even the humidity from the human body had to be reckoned with.

After the float and the cabin of the *Trieste* had been built, they had to be taken to a deep-water port. The Italian Navy suggested Castellammare, at the foot of Vesuvius on the Bay of Naples. There the excellent shipyards of the civilian-owned Navalmeccanica could be used, with the help of their engineers and builders.

The question was, how to get to Castellammare? How to transport the cabin and the float of the *Trieste* overland? But in Italy all problems seemed to have solutions. A trucking company offered the use of a giant trailer in the interest of scientific research. They would be happy to transport the *Trieste,* for the cost of the gasoline and the police tax.

One truck with its strange cargo traveled around the shore of the Adriatic, around Venice, and south. It crossed the snow-covered Apennines, descended to the west coast, and down into the historic port of Castellammare. The float had to be turned on its side in order to pass under bridges. The cabin followed a different route, through ancient Rome, across the Pontine marshes, past the ruins of ancient Pompeii, and on to the Navalmeccanica.

It was the Swiss National holiday, August 1, 1953, when the *Trieste* was finally prepared for launching. Colors were flying—Switzerland's white cross on a red background, and the tri-colored flag of the Italian

Navy. The steel arm of a giant crane of the Naval-meccanica deftly lifted the striped body of the bathyscaphe, and swung her up and out over the water. She hung poised for a moment in midair, almost like a miniature Zeppelin.

And then a charming thing happened. As the bathyscaphe hovered in air, a flock of pigeons flew out from the top of the crane and fluttered around the *Trieste* as she settled gently down upon the surface of the water.

An Italian priest blessed the launching, baptized the *Trieste* with holy water, and placed her under divine protection. This was a memorable day for the Piccards, who had worked tirelessly for many months.

On August 11, the *Trieste* took a mere dip into the water, thirty feet, mainly for the purpose of testing the equipment. Two days later she was towed out into the harbor for a second test dive of sixty feet.

The *Trieste* responded with a precision that the engineers found remarkable.

"But it was not remarkable," Jacques said. "It was the logical result of precise calculation, by a physicist-engineer."

This descent did not furnish any fascinating material for the newsmen who were waiting when the *Trieste* surfaced. The Piccards had seen only a litter of old chains, anchors, and rusty iron on the bottom.

"What, no lost Roman cities? No Greek vases and amphorae? No luminous fish?" joked the reporters.

On the 14th of August, the *Trieste* was to dive 22

[76]

fathoms. She was towed out to sea by the heavy-duty tugboat, the *Tenace,* which had been loaned to them by the Italian Navy. Jacques rode the *Trieste* all the way out to sea for this final training dive.

The Professor and Jacques opened the hatch of the entrance shaft and climbed down the ladder into the "antechamber" of the cabin, which hung 16 feet below the surface. Through the big Plexiglas window the water appeared a delightful blue.

The Professor could hear the topside engineer's

Jacques rode on the Trieste as it was towed out to sea.

orders coming clearly over the telephone. The entrance shaft was filled with water preparatory to the descent.

"Shaft full," came the report.

The upper hatchway on deck was closed, the air was let out of two of the float tanks and replaced by 400 cubic feet of water. But the bathyscaphe hung poised; she was still too light.

Jacques gave an order on the telephone. "Pump air into the two tanks again and bring more ballast." They were going up again.

"Twenty sacks are aboard."

The whole thing had to be done over again; the air expelled from the tanks in the float. Now they dived rapidly. But suddenly they stopped; the bottom was a round, pale disk some fifty feet below. What had happened? It took but a moment for Professor Piccard to figure out the answer.

The water at the surface had been very warm, lying under the sun; but the *Trieste* had reached a cold, heavy layer. The bathyscaphe was not heavy enough to sink through this dense icy wall. When they came up, an engineer who had dived down to see how the bathyscaphe fared, confirmed this; he had found the water so icy that he had to return quickly to the surface.

Up to the surface again they went for more ballast, and then back down. The bottom, when they reached it, was a desert, and they drifted along, gently bumping as a balloon rises and sinks. The only interesting thing they saw was a large yellow sea-anemone. It appeared pale lemon-yellow against the blue-green water.

Following this dive, for nearly two weeks, rough seas and storms kept the bathyscaphe from a true deep-sea dive. It was not until the 25th of August that she was towed to Capri, where the first deep test was to be made. The *Trieste* did not tow easily, it was found, but

[78]

"yawed" considerably from side to side, slowing her progress. A sea anchor fastened to the stern helped straighten her course.

At dawn, all seemed ready. An attendant diver went down to take the protective screw caps from the ballast containers, came up, and handed them to Jacques. He and his father climbed down the entrance way, and into the cabin. Orders came over the telephone.

"Flood the entrance shaft. Pull out the pins."

"Pins out."

Professor Piccard questioned the topside engineer over the cabin phone. "You are certain the pins are pulled?" If they were not, it would be impossible to release the ballast and the bathyscaphe will not be able to rise."

"They are out."

"Good. We are ready to dive."

"You are going down," came the message from the topside crew. "The deck is awash . . . . We are disconnecting the telephone. *Buona fortuna!*"

They dropped away from the surface. But suddenly they heard a rumble as a ballast tub poured out a load of iron pellets! The diver's air tank must have caught on the controlling wire—this wire had a specially devised weak point so that it would break easily if it became necessary to jettison the entire ballast tub. The Professor and his son could not stop the flow of ballast. Up bounced the *Trieste*.

They must either return to Castellammare and make repairs—thus delaying the dive—or they could block

[79]

off the injured ballast chute, refill the ballast tub, and depend on the rear ballast supply. The day and the time were too precious to lose. They decided to refill the tub. By afternoon they were ready to dive once again.

The *Trieste* descended gently into the deeps. When the cabin lights were turned off, a blue light flooded the interior of the sphere. The blue light changed to a cold gray, then the light disappeared and the cabin became black, the black of the abyss.

Luminescent flashes appeared to rise up past the portholes as the *Trieste* rapidly sank. The depth gage showed 250, 400, 500 fathoms. The searchlight was turned on and rain of white particles, "sea snow," passed the windows, "falling up."

A dim circle appeared below. The bottom!

"Tiens toi." Hold it!

They struck bottom, but there was no shock, because they had landed in ooze, and sank more than four feet into this primeval carpet of the ocean floor. The porthole was covered with mud. The depth gage read 595 fathoms—3,570 feet. They had descended too rapidly to unballast.

Technical observations took fifteen minutes, and they were ready to return to the surface. The release switch of the rear ballast tub was turned on, and iron pellets dropped down into the ooze. Such a cloud of silt was raised as the *Trieste* pulled free of the muddy bottom that they could see nothing through the ports. The bathyscaphe rose swiftly and smoothly, without oscillation. Forty-five minutes after leaving the bot-

[80]

tom the Piccards could see the blue of surface waters shining through the portholes. The surface nudged them with a gentle bump.

It had been a very satisfactory dive—595 fathoms—but a hysterical press reported that the *Trieste* had barely escaped a catastrophe because a compartment had lost its gasoline.

The bathyscaphe did not dive again until late September. She was towed by a tug out from Castellammare, and with a newly installed keel, she towed much faster and easier than before. They were bound for the Isle of Ponza and a dive into the deepest part of the Tyrrhenian Sea. The sky was overcast, the wind increased as night fell, and waves broke over the *Trieste* as she followed gamely after her tug. At dawn, white-capped waves could be seen rolling between the *Tenace* and the bathyscaphe.

It was no day to dive. Nevertheless Jacques and an engineer managed to breast the sea in their rubber boat and reach the *Trieste*.

How quiet the waters would be below! But to fill the tanks with gasoline was impossible! What had happened at Dakar was a never-to-be forgotten experience.

An attending ship, the *Fenice,* poured oil on the waves hoping to calm them, but it did not help. The flotilla returned to Ponza, seeking shelter in the lee of the island's steep cliffs.

A day later Jacques and an engineer took the *Trieste* down for a trial submersion, to see if she had suffered any damage from her buffeting in the waves. She had not.

The following morning they set out once again toward the deep Tyrrhenian site for a plunge into the abyss. On board the *Fenice* were some fifty or sixty journalists who were invited by the Italian Admiralty to witness the deep dive.

Strict checks were made on every possible cause of failure of mechanisms and instruments. The ballast-tub magnets were closely inspected. The trained personnel who had helped to build the bathyscaphe were transformed, as Professor Piccard said, "into able-bodied seamen" who attended the *Trieste* with infinite care.

It was a dark, rainy morning and after they left the shelter of the island the waves mounted. Captain Zanki, military head of the expedition, ordered the ships to halt when they arrived at the place decided on for the dive. "A medium swell," he said. The sea was not rough for a battleship perhaps, but would it be possible to service the *Trieste?*

The Professor, outfitted with a life jacket, negotiated the ship's ladder and managed to get into the launch without stepping into the sea. Jacques helped him aboard the bathyscaphe. They entered the tower and went down the hatch. The 365-pound door closed behind them. Their friends were on the stormy surface; they were descending into regions of calm and eternal night. The deep dive began. What did father and son feel as they descended, deeper, deeper—250 fathoms, 500 fathoms, 750 fathoms!

"There was nothing to cause us anxiety," the Professor wrote afterward. "Neither my son nor I could believe in the possibility of a fatal accident . . . . We had confidence in the law of nature; we had only to turn a switch, and return to the world above."

And yet, he confessed, there was something awesome and impressive in watching the depth gage trace their descent. "Those who have come back from the kingdom of shadows," he said, "can be counted on the fingers of one hand."

At 508 fathoms they turned out the cabin lights. Through the porthole luminous dots, like small galaxies, glowed and disappeared. Across the field of vision a phosphorescent fish, a brilliant creature surrounded by a halo of light flashed by like a shooting star.

They lit the 5,000 candle-power projector, a mercury-vapor lamp, and a million shining dots appeared. But this was not a zoological journey; it was a dive to determine what depth they could reach.

After awhile they had to change the containers of soda-lime that renewed and kept the air pure. There were plenty of fresh containers in the bunker under the flooring. They took turns watching at the porthole or observing the instruments. A sudden rocking indicated they were nearing bottom. They threw out ballast to ease the shock of striking bottom.

The iron pellets flew past the porthole; but the bathyscaphe continued to sink. There was a moment of something akin to a chill, until the water suddenly swished before the porthole. The descent had stopped.

They had reached bottom and landed once more in ooze on a dreary plain in the sea.

The pressure gage registered 1,732 fathoms (10,392 feet). They had proved what the bathyscaphe could do. No need to linger. They threw out more ballast, and rose swiftly.

A gentle rocking notified them that they had risen once more to the stormy surface. Wavering circles of light flickered over the cabin floor. As soon as the entrance shaft was emptied of water they would be able to leave their cramped cabin.

Jacques opened a compressed-air cock, and the water in the entrance shaft spurted from a discharge pipe in a geyser. The *Trieste* was blowing like a whale. When the entrance shaft was clear, the two Piccards climbed up to the deck, which was covered with ballast. What had happened? In a moment the Professor knew the answer.

They had released the ballast while still going down. Spreading out in a wide cloud as it descended, the shot fell more slowly than the *Trieste,* and when the *Trieste* came to rest on the bottom of the sea, the shot had settled on her decks.

On the surface once more, Professor Piccard bade farewell to the *Trieste.* This would be his last deep descent. From then on his son would be the pilot and Professor Piccard would be only an observer.

There was such a heavy swell on the surface it was difficult for the Professor to transfer to the rubber dinghy which had come to take them off. It was far more difficult, he was thinking, to make a crossing over to the *Fenice* through the heavy sea than it had been to make the descent. When he reached the *Fenice* he reported the depth the *Trieste* had reached, and the news was flashed around the world by radio. Within a few hours congratulations poured in from all over the world.

A tremendous welcome awaited the two Piccards at Ponza, but it was the Italian Navy itself that ren-

A tremendous welcome was given the Piccards when they landed.

dered the greatest homage to the success of the bathyscaphe *Trieste,* and to its creator and pilot. As Professor Piccard and Jacques were about to leave the *Fenice* at Ponza, a series of six shrill blasts from the boatswain's whistle saluted them.

"But those are the honors given an Admiral," murmured one of the officers.

Admiral Girossi nodded. "Admirals of the abyss," he replied. "They deserve it."

At the port it seemed as if the entire population were out to meet them. The mayor of Ponza, who had been on the *Fenice*, had radioed ahead the news of the success of the *Trieste*. Flowers were showered upon the Piccards as they went through the streets to their lodgings. A dinner was tendered them by the municipality and they were presented with the sword of a swordfish, a trophy brought back from the Red Sea by a Ponza fisherman. At Castellammare there was a reception and a procession through the streets of the town. The Piccards were made Honorary Freemen. They received another triumphal reception when they returned to Switzerland.

The *Trieste* had, under many varied conditions, proven her worth. All the instruments had worked "to perfection," her most meticulous critic reported. Her float had withstood very bad weather, and as for her cabin — the Piccards pronounced it "a real jewel of Italian industry."

The *Trieste* was drydocked for the winter at Castellammare. She was ready, Professor Piccard felt, to serve science. She had conquered the Mediterranean, and must go on to the deep abyss.

Chapter 5

The Whale and the Bathyscaphe

For many centuries man has tried to find a way to remain under water, but of all creation only the mammoth whale has dived with impunity from the surface into the "vasty deeps." Leviathan, as the Old Testament named him, by sheer weight and power plunges down into the black realms. Great Leviathan, the largest mammal of Earth! He scarcely feels the pressure of the deep upon the mass of his enormous, streamlined body, and he carries within his lungs enough oxygen to last for long periods of time.

With the *Trieste,* a man-made deep-sea boat had appeared, daring to rival the whale. Though it was scarcely 50 feet long, its cabin a little more than seven feet in diameter, it too, was able to withstand the pressure of the depths. It, too, carried its own life-sustaining oxygen. It, too, could rise at will to the surface.

It took millions of years for the whale to become adapted to the sea after having once been a land animal, and he must have grown vastly after entering the wide oceans which he had elected to roam. From ancient times man had a yearning to return to the sea; but only by shipwreck did he ever enter the abyss, and dead men tell no tales.

After centuries of trial and error, (mostly error), man finally developed such diving equipment as the oxygen tank and flipper-feet. These have been made popular by such famous skin divers as Jacques Cousteau and Frederic Dumas. The submarine, from primitive beginnings, was developed during World Wars I and II into the deadly weapon that could strike at an enemy from beneath the waves. After World War II, atomic submarines were developed that could dive under the North Pole or circumnavigate the globe.

Although the submarine can "hear" by means of its sensitive sonar equipment, it is "blind." It cannot reveal the wonders of the ocean to the eyes of man. The submarine is a sealed vessel, and it is limited to a depth of about 1,000 feet.

The windows of the bathyscaphe, however, permit man to see the mysteries of the abyssal depths. They can reveal to the scientist three-quarters of the almost unknown regions of Earth.

Auguste Piccard built a cabin with two observation windows, a floating laboratory that could withstand depths even greater than the mighty whale can sound. Forged in a foundry at Terni, Italy, the cabin of the *Trieste* was of special structural beauty and endurance.

From the moment the giant ball of glowing, incandescent steel was lifted from the dazzling furnace and was transported on the arm of a big crane to the great press, it was a spectacle, a vision, of man's mastery over metal. Under 12,000 tons of pressure, the whitehot steel was flattened again and again until a wide disk was shaped.

A hemispherical die moved down over the disk and forced it through a steel ring, forming the two halves of the *Trieste's* sphere. Engineers and workmen, carefully masked and shielded, gathered to watch while the cabin of the *Trieste* was being forged. A forging so large, but so precise, had rarely been attempted.

After forging it was readied for the final treatment. Fired once more to a burning red, the hemispheres were dipped in hot oil and returned to the furnace for tempering. They were then gradually cooled at carefully controlled temperatures. Hard, yet malleable, the steel spheres emerged. This tempered steel was checked and tested again and again.

This steel was destined to endure great strain — the abyssal ocean. From this steel the cabin of the *Trieste* was constructed by the finest craftsmen in Europe. It was developed eventually into a vehicle that carried the pilot of the *Trieste* down into a new world, and brought him international fame.

The cabin of the bathyscaphe was air-conditioned.

Provision was made, too, for absorbing the water that would regularly be exhaled from the passengers' lungs, and the perspiration they would give off. Two snorkel tubes were provided to let in fresh air when the bathyscaphe surfaced, before the cabin could be opened.

The cabin was lighted by six small incandescent bulbs set in the white-painted ceiling. They were low-power bulbs, providing enough light to see the white instruments clearly, and yet not enough to dazzle eyes that were accustomed to the black depths outside. As for the searchlights, these were placed outside the cabin for better visibility.

Under the sea the visibility is about sixty yards, therefore the floodlights were placed so as to cross the visual field in a narrow cone at that distance. Anything entering that illuminated cone shone against the black background of the sea.

The Plexiglas windows of the *Trieste,* like those of the *FNRS 2* and the *FNRS 3,* were of unusual clarity. They were placed on opposite sides of the sphere, the larger window in the entrance shaft at the rear; the smaller one opposite it, and slanting down toward the sea bottom.

The massive door of the cabin, although weighing 325 pounds, moved easily on its hinges. The two propellers which drove the bathyscaphe horizontally through the sea or over the ocean floor were mounted on the sides of the float near the top. They were controlled by a switch within the cabin.

The source of power of the electrically operated

instruments was a number of fairly small batteries with cells of silver-zinc. These were installed in the cabin where they could be readily recharged.

A lack of money prevented additional dives for the *Trieste* during 1955. The amount of money needed for a single dive was not astronomical, but could be called, rather, abysmal — discouraging to research. The cost of a 5,000-foot dive was about $1,000. Ballast alone cost $300 a ton, and about two tons were needed for each dive. Even if the towing tug and an escort vessel were supplied free by a friendly navy, there would still be the initial cost of the gasoline. The gasoline, however, was conserved in the float tanks of the *Trieste,* and could be returned at the end of the season, with perhaps a loss of only about fifty dollars' worth.

The most expensive item was the batteries. The small silver-zinc batteries cost $12,000 a set. Added to this were the wages of the topside crews, the air-purifying chemicals, the compressed air and oxygen, handling gear, and so on.

In 1956 funds were supplied by Swiss and the Italian organizations for the *Trieste* to resume her services in scientific research. Professor Pollini would again accompany Pilot Piccard.

During one deep dive with Professor Pollini and Jacques in the cabin, the floodlights went out when they had reached 3,500 feet. Jacques estimated that an hour's work would be needed to repair the circuit. Professor Pollini wasn't the least disturbed. "Take your time," he said cheerfully. "I'm sure there is no more restful place to wait."

When the lights went back on, Professor Pollini quietly resumed his intense study of the ocean floor. He noted the sediments that had been piled layer after layer during hundreds of centuries. Interspersed with layers of rock dust he noted tiny perforated shells of foraminifera, so minute they looked like fine dust. It was into foraminifera ooze that Jacques and his father had settled on their first deep dive off Castellammare.

On another occasion, Jacques and Professor Pollini descended together in the center of the Tyrrhenian Sea to 12,110 feet. This was the *Trieste's* deepest dive up until that time. No one had ever gone so deep before.

While Jacques and Professor Pollini were making their dives, other things were taking place which were to affect the *Trieste.* The year before, Jacques had flown to London to appear on television and to address a group of engineers. One of the men who heard Jacques' speech was Dr. Robert S. Dietz, an oceanographer attached to the U. S. Navy's Office of Naval Research in their London office. Dr. Dietz told Jacques that he was extremely interested in seeing the *Trieste*, and he thought that the Office of Naval Research might also be interested in the *Trieste.* He accepted Jacques' invitation to come to Italy.

For a long time Jacques had hoped to attract the attention of the United States Navy. But this had seemed almost hopeless. Only a few miles across the Bay of Naples from where the *Trieste* was berthed, the U. S. Navy's Sixth Fleet had its headquarters. Yet only one officer had been curious enough even to cross the bay and pay a visit to the bathyscaphe.

"Of course!" Jacques wrote later, "the *Trieste* was a deep ship that could neither fight, nor run fast, but merely sink to the bottom and rise again! It would take a marine scientist to appreciate the *Trieste*."

But suddenly the Navy did seem to be interested. Dr. Dietz visited Castellammare and with him came Dr. Thomas Killian, from the Office of Naval Research in Washington. Dr. Killian invited Jacques Piccard to come to the United States, to visit Washington, and to see all the U. S. oceanographic institutions. Dr. Dietz said he would accompany him and would try to explain to officials of the Office of Naval Research what the bathyscaphe could do to advance knowledge of the sea.

Dr. Dietz had impressed Jacques and his friends at the Naval meccanica. His quick appreciation of various devices of the bathyscaphe endeared him to the young French engineer-economist.

"He understood in a moment the spring-suspended double valve for pressure compensation," Jacques recalled later. "This valve enabled the hull to 'breath.' It admitted a controlled flow of water into the float during the descent."

At this time there was not any thought of into what particular depths the *Trieste* would plunge. That lay in the lap of destiny. Nevertheless destiny was already pointing a finger at a definite spot. Several years earlier a British ship, the *Challenger II* had made soundings in the mid Pacific and discovered the Mariana Trench, the greatest depth known in all the vast reaches of the seas. Nearly 36,000 feet deep it lay, about 200 miles southwest of Guam. They had named it "The Challenger Deep."

A wonderful sounding name! It stirred the imagination. The deepest abyss known to man! But although it echoed through Jacques' mind, he had more immediate things to claim his attention. First there was that invitation to visit Washington!

Chapter 6

Dreams That Come True

Man is just beginning to learn about the sea. Many facts are still to be discovered about the great masses of water which cover three-quarters of the globe.

Some oceanographers have been surveying the mountains beneath the sea. Others have been concerned with the possibilities of developing additional food resources in the sea, with the conservation of fish and oysters, with the transmission of underwater sound, with the penetration of cosmic rays through water, and with the theory that the continents actually drift through the seas.

Of all these things Jacques Piccard was acutely aware. "The sea's surface is a frontier," he has said, "a frontier separating man's world from the realm of *inner space*. It is the ceiling of another world."

When Jacques came to America in the early part of 1956, he seemed to find everywhere an awakened and lively interest in the sea around us. The oceanographic institutions and laboratories were eager to embark on deep-sea research.

He went first to Washington and attended a meeting of the National Academy of Sciences which had attracted more than one hundred American oceanographers to hear discussions of "Aspects of Deep Sea Research." He and Robert Dietz presented papers on the development and function of the bathyscaphe. The oceanographers later passed a resolution declaring, "The scientific implications of this capability [the bathyscaphe's] are far reaching."

Jacques spent a hundred days in America. He crossed its vast plains, and its mountains. He saw its towering cities. He experienced the warm and friendly interest of its scientists and the speed and enterprise with which things were done. There was less caution, he felt, and more readiness to accept new ideas in the United States than in Europe.

In February of 1957 the Office of Naval Research gave Jacques a contract that would enable the *Trieste* to make fifteen additional dives to the bottom of the Tyrrhenian Sea. A group of American oceanographers would be selected to make the dives, and European scientists would also be invited to take part.

The *Trieste* was no man o'war, she was no submarine,

but was she a practical under-sea laboratory from which valuable observations could be made? This was a practical question to which the Office of Naval Research wanted an answer. It would cost quite a bit to finance the bathyscaphe. Was it not safer and less costly to conduct oceanographic research by echo sounding, by taking cores of silt deposits from the ocean beds, by thermometers, winches, and buckets?

These questions were soon to be answered. In the spring of 1957 a company of oceanographers and underwater sound specialists from all over the United States converged on Castellammare.

Here was a learned delegation which would be able to assess fully the capabilities of the *Trieste*. Not one of the scientists questioned or doubted her safety. They were interested in her structure, and they wanted to know if there was enough room for their equipment. If the cabin could accommodate Jacques and his father, who was almost as tall as Jacques, there should be room, they joked, for all sorts of gadgets!

The assembled scientists arranged the program for the summer's dives. Each one was excited at the prospect of descending for the first time into the deep sea. As for Jacques, he was praying that everything would go successfully, and that the future of the bathyscaphe would be assured by this summer's performance.

Dietz had told Jacques that one possible result of the dives he was making that summer was that the Navy might ask him to make further dives into even deeper water. Possibly these dives would lead to the chance of making a descent into the abyssal depths. Everything depended on the future decision of the Navy. If the summer diving proved rewarding, then — the Challenger Deep.

Dr. Nils Jerlov, of the Oceanographic Institute at Gothenburg, Sweden, was assigned to make the first three of the series of dives at Castellammare. On July 1, 1957, the first day of the International Geophysical Year, he and Jacques began the series of descents sponsored by the Office of Naval Research. The Swedish scientist, who was investigating the extent of sunlight penetration into the sea, enjoyed an opportunity that science had not offered him before.

Looking up through the *Trieste's* window to the sunflecked ceiling that separated the world of air from the kingdom of water, Dr. Jerlov watched the dancing disks of golden light. He reveled in the lovely blue light that penetrated the cabin, and watched the blue grow deeper and deeper as the bathyscaphe sank and the sunlight was gradually absorbed in the depths.

On another dive, Jacques was accompanied by a scientist who was studying the animal life of the steep cliffs of Capri's south slope. A long smudgy smear was traced on a depth recorder as the *Trieste* sank. Near what he thought was the bottom, Jacques discharged some ballast and the *Trieste* settled softly. But they were not on the bottom.

Looking downward through the front window, Jacques could see that they had perched on a narrow shelf. Below them a steep and lumpy slope disappeared into the depths. Before he could do anything, the shelf collapsed, and the *Trieste* slid down the bank of slippery mud. Through the walls they could hear the sound of metal banging on rock.

They had started a submarine avalanche. Mud and sand poured around them; the windows were clouded with swirling turbulence.

Without waiting to observe this phenomenon any further, Jacques switched on the forward ballast tank and peered out the window to see how fast it fell. It did not fall at all!

The *rear* ballast switch then! With a welcome rumble, the ballast poured out. The other valve must have been plugged with the sand and mud they had disturbed. The *Trieste* gradually lifted itself from the avalanche, and before long was once more in the sunlight.

With relief Jacques reflected that if both ballast valves were plugged, he would have been able to release an entire ballast tub with an emergency mechanism. But this would have meant going all the way back to port for the installation of a new tub.

In one of the most interesting and fascinating dives of the summer, Jacques was accompanied by an acoustical scientist, who wanted to use the *Trieste* as a stationary laboratory. He wanted it to hang motionless and noiseless in mid-water over a 1,700-fathom basin in order to study the surrounding field of sound. It was theoretically possible to keep the bathyscaphe stationary by alternately jettisoning gasoline and then

[103]

ballast, but Jacques knew that it would be impossible to keep the bathyscaphe steady and silent for any length of time. It would need to be adjusted constantly.

Jacques solved the problem of perfect stability by anchoring the *Trieste* to the surface! He attached a very thin thousand-foot line from the *Trieste* to a raft of gasoline-filled plastic bottles which floated on the surface.

The bathyscaphe dangled motionless in mid-ocean, and in perfect silence. With sensitive hydrophones they picked up strange sounds from the "silent" sea. They heard the snapping of shrimp, the chuckle of certain fish, and a variety of groans and whistles. The *Trieste* proved to be an ideal listening station, far quieter than a surface vessel.

The acoustical scientist rarely looks out the windows on a dive, Jacques found, for he is busy writing down his measurements and columns of figures. One of them in fact, spent hours on his knees with his instruments in the cabin of the *Trieste*. When at last he rose he said, "I guess that's all. We can go up now."

Jacques, surprised, asked if he didn't want to look out, for a remarkable seascape stretched all around them. "This is a rare opportunity." said Jacques.

"Oh, I suppose I should take a look," replied the acoustician, still absorbed in his own special data.

But the marine biologist would scarcely turn his eyes away from the porthole. As the bathyscaphe descended through layers of deepening water his eyes

The Trieste dived smoothly, down below the twilight zone.

would be glued to the Plexiglas. When the craft entered the twilight zone Jacques would turn on the floodlights, and then it would seem as though the *Trieste* were going through a snowstorm. Fine little white specks flew past them. The white specks included zooplankton—those microscopic animals of the sea—and a rain of dead animal and vegetable matter that descended to the sea floor.

Below 1,000 feet, many small luminous creatures began to appear—some glowing blue and green, some wearing rows of shining disks along their flanks, and some looking like highly illuminated cruise ships. The Mediterranean is not as full of life as the Atlantic and other oceans, but there were nevertheless enough bioluminescent creatures to make a dive fascinating.

Jacques reported that at 1,600 feet there was still a trace of cold gray light which usually faded into deep impenetrable black another hundred feet down. The human eye is amazingly adaptable, he found, and can detect light that is only one-billionth as strong as full daylight. On a few occasions, Jacques found that his dark-accustomed eyes could detect light in the Mediterranean at a depth of about 2,000 feet.

In a world where the light is absorbed and the spectrum changes from the clear blue near the surface down to the utter black of the abyssal zone, where the red is quickly absorbed and blood looks green, the searchlights of the *Trieste* were the first gleam from the upper world ever to flash upon these still and timeless depths.

The fabulous monsters of the past, so confidently

pictured by medieval artists, did not materialize, much to the disappointment of news reporters and probably of the public at large. There were no scaly serpents, no half-human fishes, no "sea monkeys" like those depicted in ancient drawings.

And yet the true wonders of the oceans were fascinating—the vast masses of minute and microscopic life, the extraordinary self-illuminated deep-sea creatures, and the almost incredible devices for survival. The Angler fish, for example, had his own fishing pole hanging from his forehead with a gristly fishing lure at the end.

When Jacques returned to Washington in 1958 he found the Navy seriously considering a descent into the deepest waters of the Mariana Trench. The preliminary steps had already been planned.

"The Navy has a big base at Guam and it is equipped with cranes and tugboats," Jacques was told. "And it is only two hundred miles from the Challenger Deep."

Two hundred miles! Big ocean, big concept, big Navy! A pretty tough tow for a bathyscaphe! But Jacques had already decided.

"*Pourquoi pas?*" Why not?

One scientist wanted to know if the dive could be made with the *Trieste* as she was.

"Yes," said Jacques without the slightest hesitation. With the new Terni sphere it could. An unmanned test ought to be made first, with a robot pilot. The margin of safety would be narrow, but they would keep within it.

If the test failed? . . . . The world would be minus one bathyscaphe. However, it would make a terrific explosion down below, what with the float *and* the sphere.

Jacques knew that this would be no easy venture. What of that two hundred mile tow from Guam to the site of the dive? It would be through rough seas, far from land, with trade winds and typhoons against them! It was a sobering thought.

Chapter 7

New Worlds To Explore

The United States Navy was going to buy the *Trieste !* Jacques Piccard was to go along with her as consultant, and Giuseppi Buono, the topside engineer who had been with Jacques at Castellammare, would assist him. The Professor and Jacques did not really want to sell the *Trieste;* they had hoped rather to lease it for a period of three years. But the Navy wished to own her outright.

There were only two bathyscaphe pilots in the world at that time. They were Jacques Piccard and George Houot, of the *FNRS 3.* Therefore, there was a stipulation in the sales contract that Jacques would train two other bathyscaphe pilots.

Jacques hastened to Castellammare to prepare

the *Trieste* for her voyage across the Atlantic. The *Trieste* must be repainted and refitted with new parts to replace those which were worn. The cabin must be removed from the float, and both sections packed in separate wooden cradles for shipment aboard the *USS Antares* of the Military Sea Transport Service. It was a long trip, by way of Norfolk and the Panama Canal, but eventually the *Trieste* reached her new base at the Navy Electronics Laboratory at San Diego.

The *Trieste* looked like a striped water-bug among the vast aircraft carriers, the great seaplanes, destroyers, and submarines lying in San Diego harbor. And yet not one of those other craft could dive into the abyss. Hans Christian Andersen might have made a story out of this situation.

There was a flood of publicity when the *Trieste* arrived in San Diego. Newspapers splashed their front pages with pictures of the bathyscaphe and its crew. Every test dive in San Diego harbor was given full coverage.

The *Trieste* had to have special docking facilities and special mooring sites because of her 20-foot draft. A special dry dock equipped with scaffolds and a cement apron, and countless "accessories" had to be made ready. An old building was remodeled and an additional one was built just to house gear and equipment. Although only a few people had been allowed to come close enough to even touch the *Trieste* in Italy, in San Diego a specialist was assigned to nearly every task.

One thing that caused Navy officials great concern was fire safety. After all, there were 28,000 gallons of aviation gasoline in the float as she rode at anchor in the harbor, and should she be accidentally rammed by one of the Naval vessels, the result would be disastrous. Even when the gasoline was pumped out there was a danger that explosive fumes might remain in the compartments. Would workmen dare to light welding torches near the *Trieste?*

The American experts struggled for some time with this problem. Then they were reminded of the method that had worked perfectly in Italy. All that had to be done was to blow compressed air through the empty float. They tried it; and it worked.

There was the problem of ballast. "Iron sand," as Professor Piccard called it, was used in the United States for sand blasting, and samples were ordered from all over the country. But the electromagnetic equipment of the *Trieste* would not function with the American shot. It was apparently too fine; too different, at least, for the *Trieste* equipment. It became too magnetized to fall out of the tub, or else it would not stop falling when the magnet was reset.

The only thing to do was to send back to Italy for the original shot for which the apparatus had been designed. This was done and now at last all preparations were finished. In December of 1958 they were ready to dive, after the usual harbor test. At the last minute Jacques found that Washington had given a journalist the coveted extra place for the first dive in order to write an eyewitness script for television.

There was little to see on this particular dive off San Diego. There was so much mud and silt in the water that it was impossible to take photographs from the bathyscaphe. The story, which had been announced in advance, had to be canceled. Of course, there was a great deal of disappointment, but the journalist did not give up. He got another authorization from Washington, but the *Trieste* went into dry dock before he could make another dive.

The sea region around San Diego is both fascinating and unusual. The Continental shelf off California is much narrower and steeper than the shelf off the Atlantic coast. It is furrowed with deep canyons that are but a short distance from shore. Some of these canyons reach into the estuaries of rivers. The Monterey Canyon, one of the largest, cleaves the slope for a hundred miles and is over 6,000 feet deep. These strange fissures, however, have been found in all oceans. The *USS Nautilus* discovered a channel in the Barrow Canyon which led them beneath the Arctic ice on her two-thousand-mile journey across the Arctic Basin.

There are varying opinions among geologists as to what caused these canyons. Some believe they were gouged out by glaciers during the Ice Age. Some believe that rivers cut the channels, just as the Colorado River carved the Grand Canyon. It is believed by others that they were carved by the sea with its strong currents of gravel and mud rumbling over the ocean floor.

The ocean floor off Southern California is not deep-sea, nor is it properly classified as a continental shelf. It is described rather as a sunken ancient shelf, 150 miles across and having basins a thousand feet deep. It has been called a "continental borderland." This shelf is largely covered with a deposit of phosphates from dead fish and other forms of sea life.

Unlike the clear blue of the more sterile Mediterranean, these waters are green with the microscopic growth of the sea. These floating and swimming plants furnish food and shelter for an infinite variety of animal life. In these waters the fish multiply, for plankton is the basic food of the sea. The water off California is so dense that Jacques found no visibility below 600 feet.

Another difference between this part of the Pacific and the Mediterranean is that the Mediterranean is much warmer. Temperatures in the Mediterranean never fall below 50 degrees F. because the sea is cut off from the cool waters of the Atlantic Ocean by a ridge or sill at 170 fathoms. The Pacific waters are fed by strong cold currents flowing from the Antarctic. In the deeps of the Pacific the water is icy. Sea life largely prefers cold water, and the sea floor off San Diego is alive with sea animals.

San Diego was thronged with marine scientists. The Scripps Oceanographic Laboratories, the largest in the world, were in nearby La Jolla. The Navy Electronics Laboratory (NEL for short) had impressive installations in San Diego itself. While their research was chiefly in the fields of electromagnetics, radar, acoustics, and sonar, they were concerned also with oceanography. NEL exploration teams have explored from pole to pole, and from Mediterranean to the Indian Ocean.

An experiment in which Jacques took part at San Diego had to do with one of the most profound wonders of the sea—the reason why delicate gelatinous creatures, like the jellyfish and most of the plankton, can live under terrific pressures which would crush almost anything else. Why did these weak creatures survive when Dr. Dietz's various tools and apparatus had come up as crushed and twisted masses of metal? Why did the bathyscaphe descend into the abyss and return whole?

The answer was because pressures were equalized in the Piccard bathyscaphe almost as they were in the animals of the deep seas. Water flowed through the float chambers of the float of the *Trieste,* so that no matter what pressure was encountered, it was the same inside as out. To demonstrate this, Dr. Dietz placed some eggs in a porous plastic box which he strapped to the top of the bathyscaphe. The shell of an egg is porous, and Dr. Dietz believed that it would let sea water seep through it, equalizing the pressures inside and out. That is exactly what happened, for when the *Trieste* surfaced, the eggs were still whole.

In spite of his piloting duties, Jacques had time to marvel at the strange fish of the Pacific. The black cod, sometimes called the big-eyed sable fish, appeared hypnotized by the glow from the floodlights. They lay motionless on the ocean bed basking in the search-lights of the bathyscaphe. One fish pressed its mouth against the port window, staring into the cabin.

The sea floor was covered with brittle stars, resem-bling little spiders, their five arms writhing and twist-ing incessantly as they searched for food.

A very important dive was made into the San Diego Trough, one of the deep basins cut into the San Diego shelf, with Kenneth Mackenzie of the Navy Electronics Laboratory. The NEL scientist was attempting to im-prove the precision with which underwater sound ve-locities could be measured. For certain problems these measurements must be infinitely accurate. It was known that sound velocity under water was about a mile a second, which is about five times the speed of sound in air. But many conditions under water, temperature, depth, salinity, density, or even latitude, affect sub-marine sound velocity.

To check the influence of these factors, the *Trieste* had to hover without moving at eight different levels beneath the surface. Jacques was concentrating on keep-ing the bathyscaphe as stable as possible at 85 fathoms, when suddenly there was a sharp sound as of an ex-plosion, but which he recognized as an implosion, a collapse of some one of the air-filled devices.

In a moment there was a second such "implosion." It sounded almost as violent as an explosion, and if it were of sufficient force, it might rupture the skin of the bathyscaphe with fatal results. Instruments indicated they were not losing gasoline, so whatever had caused

[117]

the noise had done no further damage. Later they found that an underwater camera attached beneath the float, which the manufacturer had guaranteed to withstand pressures at 18,000 feet, had failed.

Since the Navy Electronics Laboratory had taken over operation of the bathyscaphe, important problems regarding the *Trieste* usually received very prompt attention. It was the small things which occasionally dragged along.

There was, for example, an ancient Navy tender which had been assigned to the bathyscaphe party for ferrying between the towing ship and the *Trieste*. The tender was not originally intended for ferrying; the engine was temperamental, and the boat leaked. Jacques would have preferred one of the sturdy lobster dorries used by the commercial fishermen in the area. But the Navy seemed reluctant to replace the tender.

The day came, however, when the tender was adequately disposed of. While both the tender and the *Trieste* was being towed by a tug, the tender suddenly yawed and filled with water. The tow rope broke and the *Trieste* rode up on the little boat. The steel cabin struck the tender, instantly converted it into kindling. There was plenty of excitement, but Jacques' first thought was, what had the collision done to the *Trieste?* The bathyscaphe had apparently not been scratched, but she did have to go into drydock for a thorough examination.

In order to account to the Navy for their tender,

[118]

some relic of the lost property had to be found. Finally a bit of the gasoline tank and the compass were recovered. With these fragments, the Navy property was struck off the record as a "boat with a few missing parts."

All during the summer of 1958, the NEL went about the business of procuring and training bathyscaphe

The tender was adequately disposed of at last.

attendants. Tests continued. There was something in the air which everyone began to recognize, but of which no one had actual proof, nor any private information.

As summer drew to a close it became apparent to everyone in the bathyscaphe project that the Navy had reached a final determination to make *the deep dive.* Now the destination would be Guam, and the object—

the Challenger Deep. To Jacques it would be the greatest challenge of his life.

Curiously enough the only announcement of this project, once it was made known to the papers, was a brief story in the *New York Times* to the effect that after exploring the San Diego Trough, the *Trieste* would "search for ocean depths down to 20,000 feet." Said Jacques, after recalling the wild imagination of the stories about the *Trieste* over the past eight years, "The press has at long last permitted itself an understatement."

Chapter **8**

Destination Guam

In September of 1958, the Office of Naval Research issued Jacques a contract authorizing the construction of a new bathyscaphe cabin that would be larger and stronger then the present one on the *Trieste*. Nothing was said about the reason for the new cabin and Jacques could only guess.

He was naturally delighted at the thought of enlarging the *Trieste*. He approached the Terni firm in Italy once more, but they did not wish to make another sphere. Jacques went to the famous Krupp steel plant, at Essen, in the Ruhr. They agreed to deliver a sphere in five months. However, because their big forge had been confiscated after World War II and sent to Yugoslavia (where it was rusting away), they would have to forge so large a sphere in three sections, a central part and two rounded ends.

Back and forth between Europe and the United States Jacques traveled. Not only did he have to oversee construction of the sphere in Germany, he had also to arrange for the manufacture of instruments in Switzerland. Early in April, 1959, the sphere arrived at San Diego and was promptly stowed away in a warehouse, still in its shipping crate. While the *Trieste* was in dry dock after the collision with the tender, an order came through to adapt the float to accommodate the new sphere. It was decided to increase the size of the float by 6,000 gallons.

On July 10, 1959, a request was mailed to the Chief of Naval Operations in Washington to grant formal authorization to Project Nekton—the name which Dr. Dietz had given to the plan to dive into the Challenger Deep. The request stated that the most favorable weather in the Marianas would be during November, December and January. The request asked that "rapid handling be accorded, in order that all action desks may see it within the very limited time remaining for action."

Everything, as Jacques said, "from thumbtacks to tugboats" was included in the accompanying list. There were to be several deep-trench dives to collect underwater sound and oceanographic data. Dr. Andreas Rechnitzer, Dr. Dietz, Lieutenant Donald Walsh, Kenneth Mackenzie and bathyscaphe pilot Piccard were to take part in the dives.

[124]

The request was promptly approved.

Now everything flew!

The float was cut into three parts, sections were added, and the joints welded. The capacity of the ballast tubs was increased from 11 to 16 tons. The *Trieste* was in the water in early September. After two successful test dives, the bathyscaphe left San Diego on October 5 aboard the *S. S. Santa Mariana.*

A Navy news release at that time said: "During an earlier series of dives the *Trieste* made a 4,200-foot dive, the deepest dive ever made in the Pacific by a free-floating submersible." This was an error, Jacques knew, for the *FNRS 3* had made a dive of 10,500 feet off Japan the year before.

The Project Nekton crew arrived a few weeks later at Guam, the little island made famous during World War II, and still an outpost of the U. S. Navy. The southern half of Guam was a lovely South Sea island shore nestling at the foot of mountains; the northern half was a flat beachhead with endless landing strips, "gooney" birds (really a species of albatross), and giant Japanese snails. It was a tropical, coral island swept by trade winds, and peopled by friendly natives and American sailors.

The island of Guam lies in the eastern part of the largest and deepest ocean of Earth, one which covers a vast region that has been rocked by violent earthquakes over untold millenia. Those violent earthquakes together with volcanic eruptions, raised up the islands and folded the ocean floor into deep cre-

[125]

vasses and submarine canyons. On the western side of the great Pacific basin, along the Hawaiian chain, there is a great fissure from which lava still pours into a boiling abyss.

In past ages many peaks of submarine mountains were thrust up between Hawaii and Guam. A glacial era drew up water from the sea and imprisoned it in vast areas of ice; in time the ocean level sank some fifteen feet. Coral animals built up the half submerged peaks, creating lovely islands. Beneath the sea, great trenches were created when seismic upliftings tore islands out of the ocean bed.

These arc-shaped trenches on the outskirts of the Pacific are the deepest spots on earth; they are far deeper than the central part of the ocean basins. And 200 miles south of Guam, at the southern end of the Mariana Trench, the deepest spot in the world reaches almost through the "skin" of earth.

The Challenger Deep, *"La plus grande profondeur!"*

There is a majesty in Jacques Piccard's French description of this vast trench. Here, nearly 36,000 feet down, is the greatest depth known to man. It is deeper than Mount Everest is high, and as great a challenge to an explorer.

Lieutenant Don Walsh, officer-in-charge, soon had the base of Project Nekton established. The Trieste was assembled and quickly made ready for test dives. On the 15th of November a stout towing line was fastened to the hook on the nose of the bathyscaphe and the tug, *Wandank,* set out for the diving site. The seas were very rough, and the trip took the rest of that day and the following night.

It was the custom to begin a dive at dawn, but on this occasion it took all of two hours to uncouple the bathyscaphe from the tug. At ten minutes after ten Buono phoned from the deck of the *Trieste* to the cabin where Jacques and Rechnitzer were waiting. He was ready to flood the airtanks. In three minutes the bathyscaphe began to sink beneath the waves.

At 45 feet there were *two violent explosions.* The central ring of the sphere had shifted slightly and a few drops of water trickled in. But this was not dangerous, for in the depths the water pressure would actually hold the sphere together.

Jacques brought the bathyscaphe to a stop at 500 feet with the release of half a ton of ballast. He always did this in order to check all instruments and to make sure that the *Trieste* was in equilibrium. This was the time to resurface if all was not well, "not after you are committed to the abyss," he said. The cabin was not leaking so it was decided to proceed with the dive. The descent continued, down through the twilight zone into deep, frigid water. The two men were wet and dripping, having been drenched by 25-foot seas while coming aboard the *Trieste,* and now grew thoroughly chilled. An hour passed; the bathyscaphe had reached 1,350 fathoms. All instruments were turned off and the hissing of the oxygen supply stopped. In the intense quiet they listened for sounds from without.

A strange crackling, like frying bacon, filled the cabin. It was too deep here for the snapping of shrimp, a sound they knew, but the sound seemed to come from the waters around them. It did not come from the bathyscaphe. They became used to this noise on their succeeding dives at Guam and the sources of it remained a mystery to the end.

While the bathyscaphe was descending, Jacques had to be constantly vigilant, watching his instruments, and maintaining equilibrium. Dr. Rechnitzer, biologist and icthyologist, concentrated on the window to the sea. He turned on the tape recorder and described the dive as they descended.

"Rechnitzer speaking. The dive commenced at 1019. We are diving fast . . . At 200 meters the color of the water is deep blue."

"We have lost communication with the surface through the UQC (underwater communication) unit," Rechnitzer taped, "although I can barely hear them at times."

So utterly smooth and quiet was the descent of the bathyscaphe that only by seeing passing of luminous bodies through the portholes could they tell that they were moving. At 2,300 fathoms there were no longer any small luminous animals of the sea to be seen. At 2,900 fathoms, luminous particles reappeared in swarms. Next the *Trieste* passed through a small cloud of what appeared to be underwater butterflies. They were pteropods (snails) which fluttered prettily with little flippers. Dr. Rechnitzer compared their motion to that of a hawk fluttering over its prey before making the dive for the kill.

At 3,000 fathoms there was still no sign of bottom. More pteropods swam past, their fleshy, protruding wings moving alternately. A beautiful worm (a pelagic annelid) with many legs and a headdress like that of an Egyptian pharaoh, moved upward past the Plexiglas port.

They began to near the bottom at last. Small animals were twice as numerous at this great depth as they had been near the surface. The bottom appeared dark, with white patches, and covered with rubble.

When they touched bottom, they found it was soft, and covered with holes. There seemed to be no current on the ocean floor, at 3,100 fathoms (18,600 feet).

A new record had been made.

And so ended the first trial dive of Operation Nekton — with a leaky cabin. But this crisis would not end the project. The *Trieste* was drydocked, and a Navy repair crew fitted two rings and six bands to the sphere. Special gaskets were constructed for the seams and all connections were bolted tightly.

Work on the *Trieste* was rushed so that it would be completed during the season of fair weather. When the trade winds blew hardest and the currents were strongest, it would be too late to dive and the project would have to be put off for another year. Perhaps the Nekton crew feared that someone else might make the dive before they did, or perhaps they were determined that the Challenger Deep was *theirs* to conquer. Perhaps they were mainly fired with scientific zeal. Whatever their individual reasons, they were a dedicated crew.

By mid-December the *Trieste* was ready to dive again. A shallow harbor dive was made to test the newly bound sphere. The *Trieste* behaved perfectly.

The *Trieste* was towed out of Guam's Apra Harbor on the 26th of January, en route to the Nero Deep in the Mariana Trench, 70 miles south of Guam. This trench had been discovered in 1899 while the *USS Nero* was seeking a cable route to the Orient. The Nero Deep, at 5,269 fathoms, was long thought to be the deepest trench on earth.

Their destroyer escort, the *Lewis,* went ahead of the Nekton convoy, echo-sounding in search of a good diving spot. The precision depth recorder finally located a depth of 5,000 fathoms, or 30,000 feet. But it was planned not to try to go so deep at this time. Their aim was a thousand feet below their last dive.

The official report to San Diego following the dive stated "maximum depth attained, 4,000 fathoms. Dive duration, 5-1/2 hours. Two implosions at 19,500 feet required temporary cessation of descent."

Jacques' account was that it was a normal descent— three feet a second, which was too rapid to observe sea life. At 18,000 feet, the *Trieste's* last record, two sharp reports which Jacques recognized as implosions were heard outside the sphere.

Jacques immediately jettisoned a ton of ballast— measuring the amount by so much a second. The *Trieste* slowed and hovered at 19,760 feet.

[130]

Jacques and Lt. Walsh checked possible causes of the noise. They turned off all the equipment and listened closely. The only fault they could find was that the gasoline valve was not working, but they could discover no other damage. They decided to continue with the dive. It was found afterward that some stanchions had collapsed. A workman had neglected to drill holes in them, making it impossible for water to flow through them and equalize the pressure.

While on the surface, the *Trieste* apparently drifted away from the 30,000-foot depth for now, at only 23,880 feet, the echo sounder indicated that the bottom was less than 200 feet below them. They were dropping at a dangerous speed of 3-1/2 feet a second, too fast for a safe landing. Swiftly, Jacques cast off ballast from both the fore and aft shot buckets. The iron tumbled out of the tubs, raising a cloud around them, and bring the bathyscaphe to a full stop at 48 feet above the ocean floor.

They had reached 24,000 feet. With the gasoline valve out of commission, they had now no way to release gasoline to make the bathyscaphe heavier, to reach the very bottom. They would have to "fall" up until they reached the surface. The bathyscaphe began to rise. More ballast was thrown out to increase the rate of ascent. Except for the gasoline valve, everything was working properly.

The return to Guam was uneventful, but when they arrived at their base they were greeted with a flood of congratulations. High Navy officers cabled enthusiastic words, and already the representatives of newspapers and national magazines were flying in to get the story at first hand.

The big story was yet to come. The *Trieste* was now ready to make the dive into the Challenger Deep. What further hazards could they face other than those they had already met and conquered? Excitement grew and the atmosphere was tense during the waiting period. Journalists agreed to hold back their stories until the descent was actually made.

The descent was to be for Jacques, and for his father, the culmination of all their labors and all their hopes. It can be imagined then what was Jacques' feeling when he learned that he was *not* to make the dive.

Chapter 9

Grave Decisions

Destiny surely had pointed to Jacques Piccard to pilot the *Trieste* into the Challenger Deep. True, there must have been other aspirants for that signal honor. But Professor Piccard had invented the bathyscaphe, and Jacques had given ten active years of his youth to developing it and to finding sponsors for it. The deep dive would be the pinnacle of their united efforts.

Was he now to be deprived of what, he felt, was his moral right to make the deep descent? All the dives that had gone before had been a preparation for *this* descent into the Challenger Deep, the final test of the capacity of the *Trieste*. Furthermore, and more important still, Jacques, by the terms of his contract with ONR, was technically responsible for the *Trieste*.

[135]

How then could this decision have come about?

He had been working on the *Trieste* one morning when the news was broken to him, just a few days before the big dive was scheduled. Jacques could not believe it. Somewhat stunned, he asked for the details. No, there was no mistake; it was official.

All that Jacques could say did not affect the official order. At last he recalled that his contract with ONR specifically stated that he reserved the right to make "any dive that presents any special problems." He had never yet availed himself of this right, but he reminded Project Nekton officials of it now. A dive to the bottom of the Challenger Deep certainly presented a special problem.

The official bearer of this bad news asked noncommittally if Jacques had a copy of his contract with him. He did, and there it was, clearly written out. However, there might be some question as to just what that clause meant, and how it was to be interpreted. Messages were at once cabled to San Diego, and back, and after several exchanges the ONR confirmed Jacques' interpretation.

True, the contract had been written when it was felt to be too early to mention Project Nekton. Nevertheless the intent of the clause was clear, and Jacques was still "technically responsible" for the bathyscaphe. How could he discharge that duty if he were not present at the most important test of all, the end result of all their investment of time and money?

So it was settled, once and for all, that Piccard would

[136]

pilot the *Trieste*. Jacques felt a vast relief and satisfaction at the prompt justice of this decision.

In the teeth of wind and waves, the Nekton expedition set off for the Challenger Deep, two hundred miles of heaving Pacific away from Guam. For weeks Jacques had been going over and over his figures and formulas, checking them again and again. For four days and nights the *Trieste* was to plunge after the *Wandank,* breasting the heavy seas.

As he lay in his bunk on the *Wandank* the first night at sea, Jacques could hear the roar of the wind and the crashing blows of the waves. He realized that once again there would be only "marginal conditions" for the dive. He thought of the light and delicate structure of the *Trieste,* following behind at the end of 600 feet of cable, taking the buffeting and banging of tons of water. Two hundred miles to go—a rough mission.

They had gotten off to a good start from Guam; running before the seas they were averaging four miles an hour. But the tow line snapped. How often this had happened to the *Trieste !* Much time was lost. Still other delays beset them as the *Wandank* was unable to make more than one knot against mountainous seas on the second day.

Tossing in his bunk during the night before the dive, Jacques counted ballast bags—not sheep—in his effort to get some sleep before the big ordeal. Dive 65, which he was facing, was not just another dive, although he kept telling himself that that was all it was. No, this would be his last dive with the *Trieste*. She belonged to the American Navy, to the ONR, and the Challenger dive would be his farewell to her.

In the morning he would take the *Trieste* down into the deepest trench in the deepest ocean, and the Challenger Deep would set its mark upon her depth gage. Man would then have reached the highest and lowest spots on the earth.

All through the night, Project Nekton scientists continued to drop charges of TNT down into the great trough of the Challenger trench, trying to locate its deepest valley. As dawn approached, the explosive charges were still adding their dull roar to the sound of wind and waves. It was Dive Day, January 23, 1960.

They would not be able to dive before dawn. The descent had been planned to start at 7 a.m., but in such a rough sea, it would be dangerous to try to board the bathyscaphe in the dark. Jacques stood on the deck of the *Wandank* mentally setting the time for the descent ahead to 8 a.m. He heard the thunderous explosion of TNT and saw a geyser shoot up against the sky; it was the eight hundredth try to locate the deepest hole of the Challenger trench.

Behind the *Wandank* the lights of their destroyer escort, the *Lewis,* could be seen a mile astern. Their special echo sounder had not been able to find this unusually deep hole and they had gone back to explosion sounding. It was a tedious method, but it brought results. They had located a depth of about 5,950 fathoms.

Giuseppe Buono joined Jacques and Lieutenant

Shumaker on deck. The seas had not gone down, and the trade winds had risen. Conditions did not look favorable. Suddenly flares were dropped from the *Lewis;* they had marked the spot! The *Wandank* circled and lumbered toward the *Lewis.* As the two ships approached one another, dye markers could be seen, staining the surface of the water.

Jacques would have to make a decision soon on whether it was safe to try the descent. It was too dark to attempt to board the *Trieste* now; they must wait. At 7:15 a.m. they made an effort to launch a skiff; 25-foot waves beat them back. Finally they were able to get a rubber raft over the side, and into it clambered Jacques, Giuseppe, and Shumaker.

The decison of whether to dive or not depended on the condition of the *Trieste.* They found her deck a mess and seas washing over her. Apparently the tow from Guam had taken a great toll. The surface telephone had been carried away, the tachometerspeed gage was so badly damaged that it would not work, and the vertical current meter dangled by a few wires.

"So, do we dive, Signor?" Buono's voice, borne by the wind, put the question directly. Would it be completely insane to try to dive under these violent conditions?

Walsh was on his way from the *Lewis* in a motor whaleboat, and to the Swiss pilot it seemed a most precarious passage. Now they lost sight of the whaleboat and now she was lifted high on the crest of a wave. Walsh leaped aboard the *Trieste* like a good sailor, grabbed a stanchion, and the whale boat bounced off out of striking distance of the bathyscaphe.

"What do you think, Jacques?" Walsh asked. Used to the sea though he was, he did not like the look of things.

Jacques replied that he couldn't tell until he had checked below. He disappeared into the conning tower, and wriggled down the shaft into the cabin. The electromagnets were working and all the circuits were in order.

It was 8 a.m., and if they were going to dive that day they must start quickly. The round trip to the ocean floor must be completed before darkness settled over the sea. If the *Trieste* were to rise in the dark, she might be lost in the waves before her escort could locate her. Nine o'clock would be the very latest that they would dare leave.

Nothing could be left to chance if the dive were to be successful. Jacques was not an adventurer, thirsting for the unknown, come what might. Operation Nekton *must* be a success. His father had always descended with a calm confidence, because he relied on the laws of physics and a knowledge of what he had to expect.

Jacques carefully made the great decision. They would dive! The essential equipment was in order. The others were waiting above for his decision, and at Jacques' nod, Walsh lifted a hand in agreement. Buono scrambled aft to release the tow line, and Jacques removed the all-important ballast pins. There should be no trouble in unballasting at will now.

Jacques and Buono slid precariously about the wave-swept deck checking everything as swiftly as possible, while Walsh went below.

"Is everything ready?"

"*O kappa, signor!*" The loyal Italian clasped hands with Jacques. "*Buona fortuna.*" Good luck.

It was 8:10 a.m. Already a blanket of moist tropical heat hung over the sea. The *Wandank* was rolling and pitching a quarter mile away; the *Lewis* was rising and sinking against the horizon.

Jacques joined Walsh below, and the heavy steel door was closed behind them. The single bolt shot into place. It was cool and dry inside the sphere, but the cabin swung to and fro like a pendulum as the waves above buffeted the float. Buono was already flooding the entrance shaft.

Inside the cabin, Jacques glanced swiftly at their equipment. Instrument shelves and panels crowded the curved space of the sphere. All around him, within arm's reach, was an array of switches and push buttons which would be obedient to his touch. None of the instruments was labeled, but Jacques knew them as he did his own fingers.

With their aid the Trieste would descend safely and safely return to the surface.

Before the front window was a motion-picture camera, at the rear window a still camera, both on small shelves. The topside telephone hung beside the instrument panel, and the wireless acoustic telephone was beside the ultra-sonic echo sounder. Below the instru-

[141]

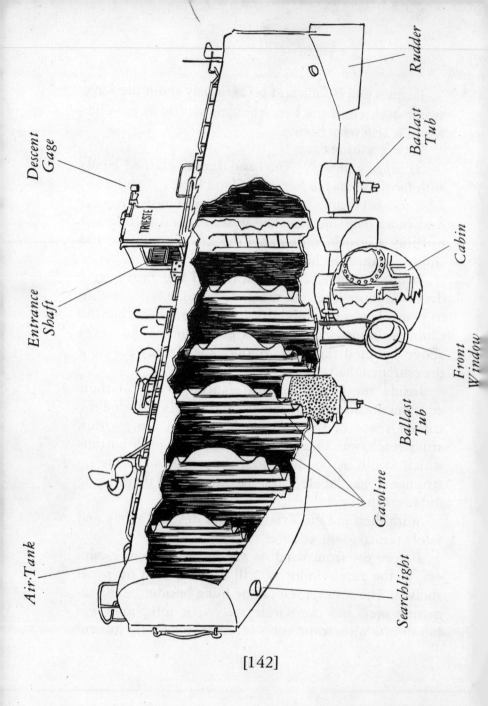

Rudder

Ballast Tub

Cabin

Front Window

Ballast Tub

Gasoline

Searchlight

Air-Tank

Desent Gage

Entrance Shaft

TRIESTE

[142]

ments were bottles of compressed air for blowing water out of the entrance shaft. There were bottles of oxygen for breathing, alkali for absorbing carbon dioxide, and beneath their feet, under the flooring, were three reserve sacks of alkali. The battery rack containing silver-zinc batteries was hung on the cabin wall.

Yes, here it all was, the assembly of every essential device. It had been checked and rechecked expertly, time after time. Jacques did not linger over it now, but swept the array swiftly with a practiced eye.

Now he glanced at his watch. He wanted to know the exact instant when the descent began.

They could hear water flooding into the entrance shaft. If the tachometer had been working they would have known the exact instant when the dive began.

Without the tachometer, they must count from the moment that the pressure gage began to move. Jacques' eyes were on his watch. At 8:23, the rocking stopped; the needle of the depth gage was quivering. All was calm; they were on their way.

"*Entre deux eaux.*" Between two waters, as Jacques phrased it. The two companions on this *grande plongee* sighed in relief.

At 340 feet the dive came to an abrupt halt, and the *Trieste* bounced gently up and down. A cold layer, a thermocline, blocked their descent with its density. Taking advantage of this pause, Jacques quickly rechecked his instruments. As a rule he would have waited for the gasoline to cool and become condensed, weighing down the bathyscaphe. But because of the

[143]

long trip ahead of them, there was no time to lose. Jacques pressed a switch which released some of the gasoline.

The *Trieste* settled through that thermocline but 40 feet farther down she again bounced upward. More gasoline was released. Twice more, at 420 feet and at 515 feet, invisible thermoclines halted their descent. Never before had Jacques met with so many solid barriers of cold.

These interruptions consumed precious time. They had descended only 800 feet by 9:00 a.m. and there was a prodigious depth to reach. They were dropping at four inches a second, but this was a tortoise's pace; it would take more than thirty hours to reach the bottom at this rate!

Thankfully they found that they had at last passed through the twilight zone and were at last descending rapidly. The Plexiglas panes revealed deep darkness outside, but not the utter black of abyssal depths. There was, indeed, at a thousand feet a faint trace of light from above, which they could see when the cabin lights were turned off.

Turning a switch, Jacques cast a beam of light into the sea. A familiar sight swept by, a snowfall of plankton streaming upward, or so it always seemed. The bathyscaphe appeared to be diving like a rocket. Walsh had tried without success to get the *Wandank* on the acoustical telephone, but he was able to reach the *Lewis*. It was always cheering to hear a voice from the surface, although *had* they wanted anything, they were far beyond any help.

[144]

Jacques' plan was to plummet rapidly to 26,000 feet, and then slow down to a rate of one foot per second until they got an echo of the bottom on their 600-foot range echo sounder. This plan would give Jacques time to jettison enough ballast to ease the shock of landing. Furthermore, it would give them time to cope with possible emergencies since nothing was actually known about the force of abyssal currents or drifts. Charts of the Challenger trench showed its dimensions as being barely a mile wide. The *Trieste* could be swept against the wall of that cleft with dangerous or fatal consequences.

At 2,400 feet, they were in total darkness, the abyssal zone. They turned off the cabin lights to allow their eyes to become accustomed to the dark. The temperature of the water dropped sharply. The *Trieste* sphere became very cold. Both men still had on the wet clothes in which they had entered the cabin.

They changed their clothes. This was not easy for a man six-feet-six, in company with another stalwart fellow in a space only three feet across and less than six feet high.

What was for lunch? On the last dive Jacques brought the lunch, Swiss chocolate bars. This time Walsh brought out fifteen American chocolate bars.

A trickle of water was coming in around one of the cable lead-throughs and was dribbling below the floor and into the bilge. Jacques and Walsh checked the leak anxiously, but it did not seem dangerous.

A call from the *Wandank* came in over the acoustical telephone loud and clear. Eagerly Jacques questioned Buono. Had the topside operation gone off properly?

"Tutto bene, signor." Everything okay. Buono's musical voice reached down through a mile of sea water. Yes, he had had time to fasten the hatch, and there was no cause for worry. It was rainy and stormy up there, worse than it had been.

The bathyscaphe was dropping now at 200 feet a minute. The leak at the cable lead-through had stopped. The wax that was used to "watertight" the lead-through expanded under pressure and resealed the opening.

Black water was rushing up past them. They were leaving all their previous records behind, and at 20,000 feet they were at the average level of the Pacific seafloor. At last they were actually dropping into that pocket of timelessness, the Mariana Trench. They had passed through the abyssal ocean and were entering the "hadal" regions, the very depths nearest to the secret center of earth.

Twenty-three thousand feet, twenty-four thousand feet; they passed the record depth of dive 64. Man had never before descended so deep. Perhaps some concern assailed their friends above, for a faint call came down to them through the sea. They were out of voice range, but unknown to Jacques, Walsh had arranged a code of tone signals to let those on the surface know above if all were well with the *Trieste*. An even number of tones meant all was well; an odd number meant bad news. Walsh sent up a double signal: "All's well."

Yes, all was well; they were on schedule at 27,000

feet down. Jacques was already dropping ballast to prevent their speed from becoming too great.

At 29,150 feet, they were as deep under the sea as Mount Everest towered above it. Here the water was clear, but not a sign of life was to be seen within the cone of the floodlights. This vast emptiness seemed like the uninhabited spaces between the planets — beyond earthly comprehension.

Beneath them lay more than a mile of water. Although no canyon walls were to be seen, Jacques was conscious of the presence of the steep walls of the Mariana Trench. He must make sure the *Trieste* did not crash into those walls. He pushed the ballast switch and slowed the *Trieste* to a speed of one foot a second.

They reached 30,100 feet. Jacques turned on the 600-foot-scale echo sounder but no echo bounced back to them. He and Walsh looked at each other. The bottom must be beyond 600 feet, then.

An extreme test was facing them — of Jacques' faith in his calculations. On paper the *Trieste* could descend a full ten miles with safety. But now they were dropping rapidly beyond the depth for which the *Trieste* had actually been tested. Moments of tense anxiety followed. They waited. In Jacques mind was the thought that the deep-ship was not merely a contrivance of steel, plastics, and batteries. Rather, it was a creation with a capacity of its own — and a will to resist the fearful pressures of the Challenger Deep.

Above their heads the gasoline contracted, admitting icy abyssal water into the float which got heavier and heavier. It seemed to Jacques that the icy water was creeping into his veins.

The tense silence in the cabin was broken only by the hiss of escaping oxygen and the hum of electronic instruments. Nothing but water, on and on, down and down into still greater depths.

Could the echo sounder be working? Looking closely, he could see a noise-recording; the graph recorded the iron ballast that was being dropped from the tub. "It is working fine," said Jacques.

What would they find on the bottom? They were, obviously, in the center of the trench and would probably escape the canyon walls. But Dietz had warned Jacques that there was a chance that the bottom would be a heavy soup of silt and mud, a turbulence of swirling currents and covered with the deposits of eons of time. Russian scientists, it was said, had tried many times to lower a camera and get pictures of the trench, but each time they got only black negatives. It appeared that the camera sank into loose silt before there was time to trigger it.

Would the bathyscaphe sink down and become trapped in this loose, dreadful muck before they realized that this *was* the bottom?

This alarming prospect was relieved somewhat by remembering what Dietz had told him. He said that the Challenger II brought up a core from the bottom—not far away from this site. The core was an ooze of siliceous diatoms—a firm floor to land upon.

Which would they find?

[148]

Chapter 10

The Challenger Deep

It was 12:06 p.m., and they had plummeted 32,400 feet down into this ancient abyss. Suddenly the sphere shook as though tossed by an earthquake; simultaneously there was a violent but muffled implosion. The two men looked at each other.

"Have we touched bottom?" Walsh asked. He was anxious, but calm.

Jacques did not think so. With apprehension they waited to see what would happen next. Everything was quiet. Jacques turned the switch of the forward searchlight; it did not light. Had the light case imploded? He studied all the dials. They were not losing gas, their equilibrium was right, and they were descending

Jacques and Don Walsh looked anxiously at each other.

just as they had been before the explosion. Should they go on down? They were so far down now they decided it would be foolish not to go all the way.

Continuing to dive smoothly at 60 feet a minute, they passed the 34,000-foot level. Water, water, everywhere! They reached 36,000 feet! Had they plunged *through* the bottom, into a new and unknown hole? They were already at the greatest recorded depth of the Challenger Deep. Could their depth gage be wrong?

Jacques watched intently through the porthole, glancing back and forth to the fathometer. Walsh recorded the depth readings as Jacques called them off. Walsh's eyes never left the echo sounder. Though an experienced submarine diver, he had never known such depths.

Black lines suddenly appeared on the graph of the echo sounder, indicating that they were nearing the bottom.

"There it is, Jacques!"

Yes, they had actually found it! The very bottom of the Challenger Deep was only some 250 feet below them. Walsh called off the soundings while Jacques awaited the precise moment to drop ballast and ease the landing.

Echoes came in weakly at 36 fathoms: 32-28-25-24- the trace grew stronger; 22 fathoms and they were still going down; 20-18-15-10 — they were almost at the bottom of the world. These were moments of tremendous excitement! On down they went, to 6 fathoms from the floor of the trench, moving slowly now. Slowly, slowly, they descended. Three fathoms.

"You can see the bottom through the port," Walsh cried. "Wonderful, wonderful!"

In the glare of the rear searchlight, the ocean floor was a flat surface of diatom ooze, a pale, sand-colored endless "beach," where no waves had ever crashed. It was a wasteland composed of the microscopic silicate shells of billions of phytoplankton that had, over untold ages, drifted down in a gentle rain from

[153]

the surface waters to pave the floor of the Challenger Deep.

Jacques and Lt. Walsh had arrived at a place where no man had ever been before. Around them was a watery plain which not even fish eyes had ever seen because it lay in the total blackness of an eternal night.

Lightly, gently, the *Trieste* came to rest a few feet above the smooth floor. Balanced delicately over beige carpeting, she hovered there, as though she were laying claim in the name of mankind to this vast, unused land, as unpeopled as the moon, and yet a part of earth itself.

But there was life, after all. Jacques had seen a red shrimp some fathoms above, and now on the bottom beneath the sphere he saw a flatfish, something like a sole, a foot long and six inches wide. A wonderful sight to see, and also an answer for all time as to whether there could possibly be any life at the bottom of the sea. Here was a vertebrate, with eyes that had never before looked on anything but utter blackness, unless at times some luminous creature passed by.

The fish stared at the *Trieste* looming above it, his round eyes suddenly protuding from the silt. It was "a true, bony, teleost fish," Jacques said. It was not a primitive ray, a relic of the Devonian age. It was a vertebrate, which is high in the long scale of evolution. The flatfish swam slowly away, half covered with the ooze, off into the unchanging dark of its world.

Walsh and Jacques turned to each other and shook hands, a mute and meaningful clasp. At 37,800 feet down, according to the Swiss depth gage, these two men had reached the bottom of earth's surface. They had joined that intrepid company of explorers who, through the ages, have discovered new areas and brought them into man's knowledge.

Walsh signaled on the UQC four times, the pre-arranged code for "on the bottom." Although they took it for granted that they would not be heard on the voice circuit, Walsh nevertheless, called out, "*Wandank, Wandank,* this is the *Trieste.* We are at the bottom of Challenger Deep at 6,300 fathoms. Over"

To their utter astonishment a voice from Heaven, it must have seemed, floated down to the two men within the steel sphere.

"*Trieste, Trieste,* this is *Wandank.* I hear you faint, but clear. Will you repeat your depth? Over."

The depth was given again and Walsh repeated after Jacques, "Our ETA [estimated time of arrival] on the surface is 1700 hours [5:00 p.m.] Over."

Down through fathom after fathom of the sea the voice that came into the seven-by-five steel chamber was thrilling with excitement. "*Trieste,* this is *Wandank.* Understand. Six three zero zero fathoms. Roger. Out."

The voice from the world above warmed their hearts and given them new energy. Their task was not yet finished. Scientific observations had to be made. The water temperature outside was 36.5 degrees. It was warmer here on the bottom than it had been at 2,000 fathoms, which had the coldest reading.

Jacques took his post at the down-slanted window

[155]

to see if he could note any bottom currents. The horizontal meter gave a reading of zero. The vertical current meter had been destroyed during the tow from Guam. Off San Diego the bottom currents had been very strong, but here he could detect nothing. The water was not stagnant, however, or there would have been no visible life at all. Life must have oxygen, and to supply oxygen, an interchange of waters is necessary, no matter how languid the current.

Now another inhabitant of this deepest of all zones became visible. The clouds of silt stirred up by the bathyscaphe settled, and a beautiful red shrimp appeared, from nowhere, it seemed.

Jacques noted the ivory carpet of the ocean floor was almost flat; there were none of the small burrows and mounds which he had seen in the Mediterranean. He exposed some film to check on radioactivity in the depth. Later they found the results to be negative.

When Walsh looked out the rear window, he found the source of the implosion they had heard on the way down. The Plexiglas window in the antechamber had a series of cracks. The contraction of the plastic and the metal under the terrific sea pressure had not been the same. The window was still in place, however. There was no danger for the moment, but Jacques knew that the cracked window might cause them trouble later.

The antechamber was the only way out of the bathyscaphe. All water must be blown out of the chamber by compressed air before they could get out. If the

Plexiglas window leaked, it would not be possible to clear the chamber so they could leave.

The *Wandank* carried a metal cover plate to seal off the window in such an emergency, but with the 25-foot waves on the surface, it would be practically impossible for divers to install it. Furthermore, there were sharks in these waters.

The *Trieste* could, of course, be towed back to Guam, and the men released there. But with the bad weather on the surface it could take up to five days to get back to Guam.

After twenty minutes on the bottom, the men realized there was only a short period of daylight left. It would be dangerous to surface at night; they must go up at once. Jacques released 800 pounds of ballast. The two men took a last look at the sea bottom as the bathyscaphe began to rise. The bottom fell below the range of their searchlight, and was returned to the eternal night that had been momentarily interrupted by the arrival of this strange craft from the surface.

It was seven miles up—to the thunderous sea, the sunlight, and the world of mankind.

The temperature in the cabin had dropped to 50 degrees and both men were chilled and cramped in their confined quarters. Jacques remembered that the canisters of alkali not only absorb carbon dioxide but also gave off heat. Each of the bathynauts thrust a canister under his sweater for warmth.

Looking through a porthole, they saw flecks of

white paint swirling in the turbulent wake left by the bathyscaphe as she rose. Of course, they knew that the sphere would shrink under the heavy pressure, causing paint to loosen and fleck away. This was more than Jacques had expected, however. How much had the abyss compressed her?

Chapter 11

Out of the Depth

T heir observations on the bottom completed, Jacques and Don Walsh were longing for the sight of sunlight dancing on the surface waters seven miles up. They had done what they set out to do; now they wanted to leave this alien place and return to the world they knew.

As they rose higher, the outside pressure decreased and the gas in the float expanded, forcing out the salt water. Relieved of the load of heavy water, the *Trieste* fairly shot toward the surface. From a speed of a foot a second she accelerated quickly to three feet a second. At 10,000 feet she was shooting up at four feet a second, and at 3,000 feet she was rising at five a feet a second.

Even with this great speed there was no vibration,

no oscillation, and no flutter. The *Trieste* behaved perfectly. Jacques did not relax his vigilance however, and he kept a sharp eye on the gasoline temperature gage. Gasoline cools as it expands, but heats as it is compressed. If they had remained on the bottom long enough for the gasoline to cool to the temperature of the surrounding seawater, the temperature of the gasoline would have dropped to well below freezing during the ascent.

The two explorers tried to contact the surface ships again and again during their three-and-a-half-hour ascent to the upper world. They wanted to let those on the surface know about the cracked window, so they could be prepared for difficulty. But the *Trieste* could not reach the tender. Finally, at 13,000 feet, Walsh heard the sonar of the *Lewis*. Presently they heard the *Wandank* trying to reach them, but Jacques and Walsh could not establish two-way communication.

Upward they rushed toward daylight, faster and faster. The *Trieste* pushed without hindrance through the thermocline which had halted her on the way down. As they neared the warmer waters of the surface, however, their speed slowed.

Suddenly the cabin began to rock! The float had broken through the heaving surface of the ocean. It was as though the waves were saying, "Welcome back. You have been on a long journey." Indeed, seven miles down and back; probably the longest and the most exciting fourteen miles that man could journey on this earth.

[162]

John Pflaum, the photographer of Operation Nekton, was one of the first to spot the bright, orange-striped conning tower of the *Trieste* as it bobbed to the surface. "There she is!" he cried, "There she is!" As the *Lewis* plowed to the spot, suspense gripped everyone aboard her. Why did not the bathyscaphe crew appear "topside" at once, as they usually did after a dive? Was the cabin flooded? Had Walsh and Piccard suffocated? Was the bathyscaphe bringing two lifeless bodies to the surface?

Inside the *Trieste,* both men were anxious to know the extent of damage to the window in the antechamber. They might have to remain in the sphere for several days until they could be released. They had saved most of their chocolate bars in case they were to be trapped below.

The men decided to let compressed air into the chamber very slowly, so that no sudden pressure would be exerted against the cracked window. Walsh slowly and carefully released three bottles of compressed air into the entrance shaft, while Jacques watched with taut nerves. The water level dropped steadily until it was below the sill of the Plexiglas window in the door. The cracked window was holding firm.

With the antechamber cleared, they were able to open the door. The two men scrambled up the passage and through the hatch. Sunlight splashed in their faces and the air was heavy with a moist tropical heat.

Two Navy jets zoomed overhead. They dipped their wings in salute, and whistled down the wind. An Air

[163]

Force rescue plane appeared. The *Lewis* lay just a few hundred yards away and the *Wandank* was bustling over the swells like an anxious hen to the rescue of her chick.

It had taken Jacques and Walsh fifteen minutes to empty the chamber, and when they finally appeared on deck, distant shouts rose from the *Wandank* and the *Lewis*. A small rubber raft bearing two photographers and manned by two sturdy sailors was bobbing over the waves toward them. The photographers were shouting wildly at the deep-divers.

"Wave, wave at us," they cried above the slap-slap of the waves. Jacques and Walsh waved.

It was a gesture, Jacques said, not for the papers, nor for an interested posterity, but of gratitude for their success, and above all for their return to the sunlit surface. The expressive face of the young Swiss was tense, clearly showing the strain of the hours in the depths. Lieutenant Walsh appeared as calm and unmoved as ever.

Not long afterward an American flag enclosed in a plastic box was consigned to the depths at the very site of the dive, to lay token claim to the Challenger Deep. As the flag was dropped from the deck of the *Wandank*, Giuseppe Buono, with a gesture of affection and bravura, cast down his cap, bearing the white, red and green Italian flag, after the red, white and blue of America. Thus he paid tribute to the part that Italy had played in the career of the *Trieste*.

The return to Guam was a triumphal procession—

and an opportunity to rest for the two men. A few days after their arrival at Guam, a U. S. Navy plane came to fly them back to the United States. Far above the ocean's surface they could look back toward the spot of their descent. The waves would continue to roll over the trench which so long had been covered and secret from man, but which now forever he would be aware of.

A few days after their arrival in Washington, the two bathyscaphe divers were called to the White House for an official recognition of their contribution to science—an achievement that ranked with those of the great explorers of history. President Eisenhower presented awards to the tall, modest Swiss explorer of the deeps, and the sturdy Lieutenant of the American Navy.

Jacques later received a letter from the President, complimenting him on his outstanding contribution in the field of oceanic research. "You have the gratitude of all the people of the United States," the letter stated, "for helping to further open the doors of this important scientific field." The letter was dated February 9, 1960, but the date that will be remembered is the date of the descent of the *Trieste,* January 23rd, 1960.

Before a year had passed, other honors and recognition came to Jacques. The Argosy Award for signal achievement in the realms of exploration was presented to him at a ceremony in Washington on February 2, 1961. Not long afterward, the Woods Hole Oceanographic Institution of Massachusetts gave a dinner in his honor at the American Museum of Natural History in New York. His book, *Seven Miles Down*, written in collaboration with his old friend, Dr. Dietz, was published, telling in exciting detail the story of the bathyscaphe and the *grande plongee*.

The bathyscaphe was the forerunner, Jacques stated, of the deep-sea craft of the future. It was so safe, as Professor Piccard was wont to say, that "the father of a family could trust himself to it with perfect confidence." And yet it was obsolete almost as soon as it had been constructed, so rapidly had technology developed.

As originally planned, the bathyscaphe included many of the features which the abyssal boat of the future will possess. It was not for want of design that these features were not included from the beginning. It was for want of money; funds were lacking.

Great economy had to be used; much thought and research went into the building of the deep-sea bathyscaphes to make them completely seaworthy, pressure-proof, and at the same time keep within a very close budget.

What has the deep sea to offer mankind? There are still many secrets to be revealed, many questions to be answered, but enough has been learned to predict a fantastically wonderful future to be reaped from the sea.

Chapter 12

Deep-Ships Of The Future

It has been said that anything man can imagine, he can do. That claim, of course, is not altogether true, although without imagination man would have accomplished very little on this earth. It is true that the wonderful imagination of Jules Verne, revealed a century ago in his book, *Ten Thousand Leagues Under the Sea,* was virtually a preview of what was to come. The twentieth century has seen many of Verne's fantastic inventions materialize.

Electricity had not yet been used for lighting and power when Jules Verne wrote his book of submarine fantasy. How great would be Verne's astonishment if he could return and see modern steel-sheathed, atom-powered, and electrically equipped submarines?

[169]

But there remain two functions of Verne's fictional submarine which the modern submarine has yet been unable to match—and may never be able to equal. The first is the ability to dive deeply, even into abyssal waters. The second is that wonderful clear window, through which Captain Nemo and his guests could look out into the fascinating flood-lit depths.

Marvelous as the present-day submarine is, its very structure, shape, and weight make it impossible for the sub to explore the depths. It remained for the comparatively fragile little deep-sea boat—the bathyscaphe—to reach the deeps, to withstand tremendous pressures, and to be able to look out upon the ocean floor. The bathyscaphe could not roam the abyss; it could go up and down, but it had only a limited horizontal range. Furthermore, it was small and cramped. But it did show the way to exploring the depths.

The bathyscaphe was not designed and planned for warfare, but for science. It was intended to be a laboratory from which to observe the life and conditions of the oceans—to observe with human eyes, rather than with photographs, or even television. Both Professor Piccard and his son asserted that if an improved bathyscaphe were to be built without worrying about cost, it would be a magnificent extension of marine research.

Jacques asserted that if it were possible to make a buoyant bathyscaphe sphere that did not require a float, it would be a tremendous advance. Stiffened steel cylinders or light aluminum alloys would make possible a craft which could descend to 15,000 feet. And beryllium, a very light metal, could be used for abyssal ships. But beryllium has two unfortunate attributes which must be overcome — it is very expensive, and it is poisonous to man. There are still other materials which might be tried: various plastics, and fiber glass.

When the day comes, as Jacques predicted, that a buoyant bathyscaphe hull can be forged, there will be a "revolution" in deep-ship design. Then there will be deep-ships of a type that will be basically different from either the *Trieste* or the submarine.

Perhaps the most immediately feasible deep-sea boat would be the "mesoscaph" that Professor Piccard described in 1954. This deep-sea boat would be able to cruise the middle regions of the ocean. It would cost less to operate than the bathyscaphe. It could carry several persons at a time as well as a large load of scientific equipment, and it would be able to cruise on the surface as well as dive.

This "middle depth" boat would make possible intensive research in the upper mile of the ocean. It would be a submarine helicopter with a rotor that would drive it down instead of up. If the motor should fail, the mesoscaph would simply float to the surface.

Perhaps the mesoscaph could be made entirely of clear plastic, allowing the occupants to see on all sides. Plastic would also make the boat very buoyant. What a wonderful panoramic view of the sea could be had from such a marine helicopter! It could hover in the midst of a cloud of luminescent plankton. The passengers could watch a mother whale nurse its calf. They could see the seals deep-diving for fish, and watch the luminous squid. They could observe the endless, relentless struggle for food as the creatures of the sea prey upon one another.

Although a plastic boat might be suitable for the middle depths, for great depths steel or titanium is necessary. For abyssal depths, the ideal ship of the future might have a titanium cabin, and be propelled by atomic energy. Such a ship would have movable arms, lifting hooks, sonar senses, closed circuit TV, and special equipment for scientific observation.

Such a deep-water craft could reach any depth of the sea and could cruise the waters of the world. This craft would be almost like the fabulous *Nautilus* of Jules Verne.

A deep-sea vessel that could dive to 20,000 feet would be able to explore most of the ocean bottoms. The deeps and trenches that reach down to 36,000 feet make up only about one percent of the sea floor.

The transatlantic ship of the future, as visualized by Professor Piccard, might be a deep-sea ship. Such a ship could cross the ocean in two days, moving through the deep and quiet waters, out of the reach of surface winds and waves. The fare would probably be a fraction of that charged by a first-class surface steamship. There would be no need for sun decks, Professor Piccard pointed out, and no swimming pools. The voyage, however, would be safe and swift, and the accomodations comfortable and luxurious.

To answer the need for a small, maneuverable underwater boat, Jacques Costeau, the skin diver, had a "diving saucer" built at Marseilles, to use from the oceanographic ship *Calypso*. This delightful, responsive little craft was able to go below the skin diver's limit of 180 feet. Only two persons at a time could ride in this boat, and they had to lie flat within it because it was only six feet, seven inches in diameter, and five feet thick. The pilot and the observer could look out through a fiber glass window that extended around the edge of the craft.

This "diving saucer" was jet-driven, powered by six nickel-cadmium batteries mounted on the outside. If anything happened to the craft, the occupants could quickly don their Scuba suits, and abandon the "saucer" to its fate. The men would escape through the top hatch, after first pressurizing the hull to the depth at which they found themselves.

While the *Trieste* was making her dives from the Navy Electronics Laboratory in 1959, an incredible deep-sea tank was being created near the berth allotted to the *Trieste*. It was "under wraps" at the time, but was later displayed by the Office of Naval Research and the Scripps Oceanographic Institution. They called it RUM, short for Remote Underwater Manipulator.

An unmanned robot, the RUM was devised to crawl over the sea-floor, obedient to its telemetered instructions, and carry out at great depths what its operator ordered. This weird and fantastic tank could crawl through the surf, place instruments on the bottom at designated places, take both still and motion pictures, and relay television pictures to the surface. Its "brain," which transmits instructions to and receives information from the RUM, is a large van filled with electronic equipment.

As the RUM crawls, its cable unwinds from a spool

The Remote Underwater Manipulator is a weird deep-sea tank.

on top of the van. The five-mile cable furnishes power for everything, as well as messages to and from the "brain." While the RUM prowls the sea floor, the cable reels in or spools out automatically so that it does not tangle. This amazing machine can "speed" up to three miles an hour, climb steep slopes, and get over foot-high interference. If there is anything higher, with good judgment, it goes around.

[174]

Its body is oil-filled, and the pressure inside is kept at equilibrium with the pressure of the surrounding sea. RUM has a mechanical arm, including a "hand" that opens and closes, and a "wrist" that rotates to either side. The arm can imitate nearly all actions of the human arm.

The arm is a sealed, oil-filled unit at the end of a boom projecting aft from the crawler. The boom rotates, pivots, and flexes. The RUM looks the most monstrous of the monsters of the deep, and would, no doubt, flatten out a thirty-foot squid like a submarine bulldozer.

But how precisely and delicately it operates! The arm reaches out fully fifteen feet from the end of its boom, feels around in front, in back, or to the side, picks up a rock, places a current meter, or does any other job that the operator at the end of the cable signals it to do. It can lift weights up to 5,000 pounds.

Four miniature television cameras are mounted in steel tubes tested to withstand a depth of 36,000 feet. RUM might be able to explore the Challenger Deep if there were a base within reach of its cable. The cameras cannot be oil-filled, but they survey the scene through cylinders of plastic, fashioned like small bathyscaphe windows. Two of the cameras look out at the sea bed which is illuminated by two powerful mercury vapor lamps. The other two observe the arm, and provide either a flat two-dimensional view or a three dimensional view.

RUM's advance over the bottom is guided by a

special sonar, which detects obstacles farther away than the TV cameras can see. When the sonar is not sending out its searching pings, it functions as RUM's "ears."

In one way or another, man, whether with the use of marvelous devices like RUM, the mesoscaph, or improved bathyscaphes, is eventually going to explore the sea from top to bottom. He will never be content to leave nearly three-quarters of the earth unvisited, so many millions of square miles of watery "space" unexploited.

Chapter 13

What Does the Sea Mean to Us?

H ow long will it take to reach the moon? Who will be first to explore Venus? These are questions which our space-minded age has been anxiously talking about. And yet, right here, on Earth, is a challenge almost equal to that of space, and far closer to us. This challenge is the ocean. It surrounds us on every side, and is a space infinitely larger than the moon.

The greater part of the ocean is less known to us today than the surface of the moon. The Pacific alone is 17 times larger than the visible face of the moon. All the oceans together possess 350 million cubic miles of space — most of it unfamiliar and uncharted.

What a vast area of earth to leave unexplored while man contemplates flying off into space to visit other planets (which appear to have little or no water). True, enough has been learned about the ocean to know that it has 36,000 foot-deep trenches, that it has ocean-long ridges, 2,000-mile-long fissures and abyssal plains. These are all very different from the surface features of the earth, and completely different from the moon.

What has formed these strange ocean features? We must understand the forces that shaped the oceans if we are to understand the history of our earth and its sister planets. Studying the living creatures of the ocean will shed light, too, on the fascinating story of the evolution of land life.

Man has always been fascinated by the sea; it is literally "in his blood." The blood of man is a salty solution containing many of the same chemicals—and in the same proportions—as sea water. It is a reminder that his predecessors crawled up out of the sea about three hundred million years ago.

And yet, in spite of the immensity of the oceans and their importance to man, the science of oceanography is less than a hundred years old. Leonardo da Vinci put his ear to an oar thrust into the sea, trying to detect sound waves traveling through water. Benjamin Franklin called attention to the fact that there was a tremendous current which carried a sailing vessel to England in half the usual time—the Gulf Stream. But it has been only during this century that the ocean has been the subject of methodical study.

The ocean cannot be taken into the laboratory, so science must take the laboratory into the ocean. In fact, it is said that the ocean is one great chemical laboratory. One of its most important chemical agents is the smallest form of life, the bacteria. Even smaller than the microscopic diatoms, the bacteria are called the scavengers of the sea, for they quickly remove all waste and impurities.

Bacteria exist in all levels of the ocean, from the sunlit zones of the surface to the very bottom. They reduce the organic matter — the dead creatures and plants — to phosphates, nitrates, and other chemicals. When the upwelling of waters carries these nutrients to the surface, the microscopic vegetable plankton flourish and multiply. These "meadows of the sea" then nourish the other living creatures of the ocean. The lowly bacteria are also agents in the making of oil. Some scientists believe that oil is constantly being formed in the bottom sediments at a rate that equals all the oil presently being drawn from the earth. This oil is too widely diffused to collect in pools, however, but it is a thought that a study of the conditions under which it is produced might help geologists in their search for deposits of oil formed in past ages.

It is known that bacteria also produce various marine antibiotics. These antibiotics undoubtedly serve a purpose in marine chemistry, for plankton appear to thrive in their presence. So far none of these antibiotics have been found useful as a drug for man, but in the immensity of the sea others may be found that will help rid man of disease.

The sea is filled with food for its creatures. It lit-

[181]

erally bathes them in it. Measureless spaces are needed to grow this food, which basically is plankton. The vegetable, or phytoplankton, which lives near the surface, absorbes the upwelling nutrients, and with the aid of sunlight multiplies into vast "meadows" upon which the animal, or zooplankton, feed.

It is estimated that plankton alone weigh more than all the other life of the sea, including whales. The name plankton is derived from a Greek word meaning wanderer, and these small bits of life are indeed wanderers, for they are carried along by the currents to the far reaches of the seas.

The giant sperm whale swallows incredible masses of the quarter-inch shrimp-like copepods that feed on the vegetable plankton. Schools of herring descend upon these floating meadows and eat their way through them without seeming to diminish them in the least. Squid eat the herring, and bass and other fish eat the squid. But all the higher forms of ocean life depend, ultimately, on the plankton.

It was long thought there could be no life in the abyssal depths. Then the bathyscaphe discovered a flatfish basking in the ooze of the Challenger Deep. The scientists who descended through the twilight zone saw more life there than they had thought possible. Because the fish of the dark abyss have no plankton on which to feed, they depend on the dead animal and vegetable matter that falls into their dark world from above.

As man learns more about the amazing reproductive

[182]

powers of the plankton, it may help him in his own search for additional sources of food for a rapidly expanding human population. Future famines may possibly be prevented by harvesting the abundant meadows of the sea.

Marine biologists have found proof of the evolution of animal forms by studying the changes in plankton as they adapt to new environments. These changes have been discovered even in the larval stages of some sea animals. This discovery, scientists say, has been the "most important biological principle to come from the study of plankton." One distinguished biologist believes that the young of any species can adapt itself to new conditions of life, changing from its inherited characteristics. In an amazing evolutionary jump, it can develop new traits in just one generation.

The study of the sea is slowly yielding knowledge of the mysterious processes of life. Life evolved in the sea, and some mammals like the whale, returned to the sea after having become adapted to the land. Others chose to live largely in the sea, like the seal and the otter. But has evolution at last ceased? No, the creatures of the sea demonstrate that evolution is a continuous process and is going on.

Some "ancient" forms of life are still to be found in the oceans. When the coelacanth was discovered some years ago it created a sensation. It was an extinct fish, a fossil from the abyssal deep, scientists believed! Its fleshy fins and large armored scales surely made it look like a creature of the remote past. But it turned out that unscientific fishermen of the East Indian coast had been pulling in coelacanths regularly — not from the abysses at all — and were selling them in the fishmarkets.

There were the "monk seals" that were thought to have been exterminated early in the 17th century; but they had found themselves a place to hide. Skin diver Jacques Yves Cousteau and some friends were told by an old fisherman of a cave off a lonely coast of West Africa where the seals hid. The divers found the seals, which were shy, but infinitely friendly; cautious, yet so full of play that they tickled the diver's legs with their whiskers.

It is well known by geologists that the seas have changed amazingly since the beginning of time, or rather, and more to the point, since the beginning of life in the sea. It is known, for example, that the seas were once some 500 feet higher than they are now. The Ice Ages came and went, and the seas rose and fell. The glaciers drew up sea water in their frozen masses and left vast exposed regions that once were sea bottom. The continental shelves must have been uncovered then.

Over the centuries since the last ice age, the oceans have recovered an estimated 300 feet of water. If all the glaciers of the world were to melt, the coastal cities of earth would be inundated. If the Greenland and Antaractic icecaps were to melt, an additional 186 feet of water would be added to the sea — 4,860,000 cubic miles of water. Fortunately, the ice-caps do not seem to be melting now.

[184]

Much of the geological history of the earth can be learned from the sea floor. Most of nature's adjustments take place slowly; man lives during vast changes that he does not even see because they take centuries to complete. Earthquakes and volcanic eruptions, of course, make themselves known at once. These violences have raised mountains in the sea, and lifted islands above the surface. But less dramatic changes — the slow sinking of some land, and the slow, slow rise of other land — is going on around us all the time. The story of past and continuing changes can be read on the sea bottom as well as on the land.

Meteorologists believe that the oceans control the climate of earth by means of cold and warm ocean currents and the winds that blow over them. It is important, therefore, to know where the currents of the sea come from and where they go. The surface currents are well charted but very little is yet known about the deep currents.

During the International Geophysical Year, experiments indicated that there was, for example, a strong counter current flowing beneath the great, warm Gulf Stream. Oceanographers were able to follow it for only a short way, and it remains largely uncharted. It is believed that there are rivers in the seas' depths with a flow a thousand times greater in volume than that of the Mississippi River.

Although there are currents in the depths, almost never do surface waves cause any stir in the abyss. Occasionally, however, there are violent earthquake or volcanic waves — called by the Japanese "tsunami."

These seismic waves have nothing to do with the surface weather, but travel across the ocean depths carrying silent destruction.

In May 1960, a violent tsunami suddenly struck San Diego harbor carrying away many piers, and wreaking heavy destruction. Wave after wave rolled in, until the harbor was covered with a seething mass of foam. In fifteen minutes the waters of the bay rose seven feet. The yawl *Saluda* was torn from her mooring lines and crashed into a Navy pier, while other vessels made haste to get away out to the open sea.

This tsunami was the result of a violent earthquake that occurred in the ocean trench off Chili just the day before. It had sent off a series of tidal waves clear across the Pacific, and in thirteen hours some of these waves had reached San Diego. The oscillations in the harbor lasted for three days. The mooring place of the *Trieste* was right next to that of the *Saluda,* but fortunately the *Trieste* had not yet been returned to San Diego from Guam, or she would have been ruined.

History has accounts of many destructive tsunamis. The pirate town of Porto Bello in the West Indies, where Blackbeard hid out, was sunk beneath the waves in the eighteenth century. It is said that at times the church bell can be heard ringing under water as waves swing it to and fro.

Man can do nothing about tsunamis, unfortunately, but sound devices *can* give him "distant early warning." The sound of a tsunami races through the sea ahead of its destructive shock wave.

The sound conductivity of the sea can be helpful to man in warning him of approaching destruction, but might it not have some other use? Are fishes aware of the distance and speed sound will travel in water? Do they have some means of communication through the sound channels already discovered? Is it possible that man will discover a new means of communication making use of the ocean sound channels?

And time? The living creatures of earth are tuned to the rhythm of time, but the sea is timeless. Only the moon-influenced tides observe time; in most of the ocean there is no day or night, little or no difference from month to month or year to year. There is no beginning, no ending.

There is no "here" and "there" beneath the sea; except on the bottom, there are no landmarks; gravity loses much of its force. There is up and down, but who can determine which is which without an instrument?

Some crabs place a single grain of sand in each ear; presumably, science says, to establish a vertical orientation, a direction finder. When the old body shell is shed the crab at once replaces the grains of sand so he can determine which way is up and which way is down. Apparently, without the grains of sand he would be on his back half the time, as was demonstrated in an aquarium supplied with iron particles instead of sand. With no sand available, a captured crab placed an iron particle in each ear. Then some inquiring scientist placed a magnet on top of the tank. The crab turned completely upside down.

But it is not only the secrets of life in evolution, of currents, of food, of weather, of chemistry, and of earth's history that are waiting to be revealed. In the abyssal seascapes that have for centuries lain undisturbed by the upper world, there are fortunes literally waiting to be picked up.

Enormous deposits of valuable chemicals and minerals can be recovered from the sea bed, once technology finds a way to collect them without too great a cost. Although the presence of valuable deposits has been known since the *Challenger* expedition, it did not seem possible to get to these open mines of the sea. With the advance of technology, however, mining the sea bottom may be a possibility. Nickel, gold, silver, cobalt, manganese, copper, and many other valuable metals are there. These minerals are all needed in the world above.

Manganese, so needed in making steel, lies about the sea floor in nodules of high concentration. The nodules run as high as 20 percent manganese, together with traces of cobalt, nickel, and copper. The nodules that have been dredged up are sometimes larger than ten inches in diameter. Since the dredges which hauled them up were not equipped to pick up larger objects, it is highly possible that they missed many extremely large pieces.

Some of the manganese was thrown up by volcanic action under the sea. Some of it was leached out of submarine rocks themselves. The manganese reacts with

[188]

dissolved oxygen in the water and is precipitated on any available rock or object as manganese dioxide. It lies all over the ocean bottom, in small grains within the deep-sea ooze, around an old nail, a shark's tooth, a piece of whale skull, anything.

The nodules grow and grow, and will continue to grow, as long as there is manganese in solution. The manganese carries the other metals with it as it encrusts anything to which it can attach itself. No one knows how long it has taken these nodules to grow; probably a long time. One geologist thinks thousands of years; and they could not grow at all without water, nor if they were covered with silt.

The discovery of the manganese nodules was virtually forgotten after the *Challenger* discovery, and was not brought to light again until the International Geophysical Year. It is very definitely possible to mine this wealth under the sea with machines that are being developed by industry.

This and other projects can be further investigated when deep-sea craft are used. Meanwhile, if the "mid-ocean" helicopter is built, one can imagine a day coming when in addition to its scientific value it would also have enormous popularity, a grand extension of the glass-bottomed boat. A trip in such a boat would be a voyage of wonder and fascination for the curious who would eagerly seize the opportunity to get a look at the infinite beauty and wonder of the sea.

Contemplating these wonders, they would be reminded of the Psalm: "Neither are there any works like unto Thy works." Or, perhaps they might remember the saying from Genesis, which Auguste Piccard often quoted, "and let them have dominion over the fish of the sea.... and over all the earth."